PSYCHOPHONETICS

Holistic Counseling and Psychotherapy

Stories and Insights from Practice

ROBIN STEELE, PH.D., EDITOR

Lindisfarne Books
2011

LINDISFARNE BOOKS
An imprint of SteinerBooks / Anthroposophic Press, Inc.
610 Main St., Great Barrington, MA 01230
www.steinerbooks.org

Cover image: *Cleansing* by Jess, 2001; used by permission
Cover and design: William Jens Jensen

LIBRARY OF CONGRESS CATALOGING-IN-PUBLICATION DATA

Psychophonetics : holistic counseling and psychotherapy : stories and insights from practice / Robin Steele, editor.

p. ; cm.

Includes bibliographical references.

ISBN-13: 978-1-58420-086-4

ISBN-10: 1-58420-086-3

1. Anthroposophical therapy. 2. Holistic medicine.

I. Steele, Robin.

[DNLM: 1. Anthroposophy—Autobiography.

2. Psychotherapy—methods—Autobiography.

3. Counseling—methods—Autobiography.

4. Holistic Health. WB 903]

RZ409.7.P69 2011

616.89'16—dc23

2011013587

eBook ISBN: 978-1-58420-104-5

Contents

Dedicated to Barrie Webster

For the love, healing and deep peace we shared and continue to share, and for teaching me the power of sounding "mmm" through the heart flow, bridging connections over the threshold of death.

> Faithfully
> I will follow your soul
> Through the gate of death
> Into the light-engendering
> time-places—
> With *love,* I will ease spirit coldness for you,
> With *knowing,* I will untangle spirit light for you,
> With *thinking,* I will linger with you.
>
> RUDOLF STEINER
> *Our Dead: Addresses, Words of Remembrance, and Meditative Verses, 1906–1924* (CW 261)

Preface

Yehuda Tagar

This book describes a process of creation begun twenty-five years ago when the first article about the potential of Rudolf Steiner's embryonic dramatic methodology for human transformation was published in London and distributed at the Goetheanum in Dornach, Switzerland. The exploration, with colleagues, of the connections between the human soul, drama, and the sounds of human speech in direct sensory experience led to my paving a new pathway for human development by creating *Philophonetics* ("the love of sound") for theater work, as well as *Psychophonetics* ("awakening to sounds of the soul") for personal development, healing, and transformation. This book is a response to the many requests made over the last twenty years for a book to be written about Psychophonetics.

Psychophonetics is making a unique contribution in the field of personal and social development, counseling, psychotherapy, coaching, and artistic therapies. By extending verbal communication to include the deep intelligence of sensory, kinesthetic, imaginative and sound intelligence, Psychophonetics enables people to observe their own experience with an objective perspective. It empowers people to become their own authority in determining the meaning of their experience and opens a broad range of options for people to choose their own responses to life challenges and to own and transform their reactions, projections, and subjugation to sub-personalities. It enables the invocation of higher dimensions of one's being, self-conceived and imagined, into everyday life, where it is needed for the possibility of new creation. Psychophonetics can be seen as training in self-leadership, which underlies all other forms of leadership, allowing the fresh entry of one's individual spirit into any moment and aspect of one's subjective experience, giving it new meaning, healing it, creating something new.

Psychophonetics is an ongoing conscious and methodical development in empathy as an integrated organ for the perception of human experience and nature. It is a genuine language for the deep heart intelligence required for conscious empathy, facilitating the understanding of our own experience as the basis for understanding others. It is a soul language, enabling a deep discourse between cognition and experience through the soul's own mode of communication—sensing, movement and gesture, imaginative perception, and the healing power of spoken sounds.

The capacity of human reflection is adequate for observing external phenomena, but inadequate for perceiving our own experience out of which it grows. For that purpose, a special organ for self-perception must be forged from its own substance. This process requires grounding of the individual human spirit in one's psychological reality, for the human "I" can see the soul of others only to the degree that it can perceive its own. We have twelve ordinary senses for sensing the world, including our own body, but we do not have a ready-made sensory organ for self-perception, even though this faculty progressively determines the quality of our functioning.

The future of humanity and the Earth depends on the development of the soul's perception of oneself and others. "See me, hear me, know me." This call for conscious empathy is the threshold between the survival and vigor of individuals, families, communities, and civilizations and their degeneration and demise. From the same "I" that separates us from old communities to become more individual in the world, a new impulse is arriving as conscious, awakened empathy toward the depth of our soul, as the rudimentary instrument for empathy toward others and nature. However, the growth of empathy requires awareness; this crucial evolutionary step can take place only in full waking consciousness and through free choice.

As a practical path for the development of empathy, Psychophonetics is a modern continuation of the Delphic motto: Human being, know yourself. In Delphi, the supplicant for knowledge was led into the earthy oracle, "the navel of the Earth," where the high priestess, in a trance and seated on her tripod above it, spoke its mysteries to the initiated priests, who then interpreted her message to the supplicant. That same depth of knowledge must now emerge from our inner soul life.

Psychophonetics is the midwife of the internal Delphic oracle for self-knowledge. Clients present a quest in good faith to the meeting. That "wish" is born out of deepened self-knowledge; a client's own body becomes the "navel of the Earth." The client's sense of self is the message rising, and the client's spontaneous gesture serves as Pythia's enigmatic ancient tongue. Clients' chosen and self-articulated meaning becomes the high priest in the domain of their own destiny. The practitioner is the supporter, facilitator, coach, companion, encourager, and midwife for these capacities.

This book shares experiences and practices of Psychophonetics counseling and psychotherapy in peoples' lives and work. One hopes it will enable readers to form their own opinion of the merit of this cultural contribution. May the Greek myth of "Persephone," which enabled Psychophonetics to evolve in the depth of human souls during the past two decades, become more accessible to the public through this welcome and timely publication. As the founder of Psychophonetics, I am very grateful to Dr. Robin Steele who initiated this book. Robin, a close colleague since 1993, is the former vice-principal of Persephone College in Australia and a Psychophonetics practitioner, teacher, supervisor and researcher. She is the first person to have completed a doctoral thesis on Psychophonetics. Robin is uniquely qualified to be the editor and an author of this book. The definitive book on the methodology of Psychophonetics and its applications is being written and will be published in the near future.

Thank you, Robin, for your pioneering work. Thanks to the practitioners who contributed chapters to this book, and thank you for furthering this work through your own development, research, and practices.

Finally, may Psychophonetics, as a creative and practical application of Rudolf Steiner's psychosophy, continue to grow, develop, and make a significant contribution to the living Anthroposophia.

Yehuda Tagar, Founder of Psychophonetics
Principal of Persephone Institute,
Hout Bay, Cape Town
June 14, 2010

Foreword

Robin Steele

We are seeking our soul and through our "I" we are illuminated by spirit. If our task on earth is based on karma and reincarnation in which our karma can emerge, then it is important to recognize who we feel connected to at a soul level, and to learn how to live and work together harmoniously—to become more alert to the karmic opportunities in every present moment. In doing this we can further develop our self-awareness and love, by learning to become more conscious in our thinking, feeling and deeds. How do we do this? How do we learn to be less reactive? What skills do we need to learn? Who can be our companion on this journey?

It is gratifying to see a steadily increasing interest in consciousness studies around the world, in which the question is asked more often: Where is the "I" in the experience of the world? Where do we find our inner light?

I remember that when I was about twenty-eight years old I had a profound experience of what I called at the time: "losing my inner light." It felt like I had lost my soul. From that time on, I began actively seeking my soul, to recover and to restore that inner light that was for me experienced in the heart. What began as a personal journey of inner development later became a professional interest in the psychological and soul aspects in teaching children, and finally in my early forties, became my vocation, when I met my karmic soul group and my destiny with Anthroposophy through Psychophonetics psychotherapy. When I decided to retire from early childhood teaching, my destiny as a counselor/psychotherapist and adult educator arrived. These two streams converged for a short time and as I ventured along the new path, I discovered that the outer world of childhood was reflected in the inner world of the adult—a place of nonverbal and creative expression that I knew well.

We are living more and more with the question of how do we encourage each other to make choices that serve not only ourselves, but also each other and the world, and how do we carry the development of the individual within the social context, so that a narcissistic development does not happen? Psychophonetics is a relational process that sees the "I" or self as central in the therapeutic context. The ethic of having this position held by the "wish" makes all the difference in knowing who is making the choices and who is making the meaning from the experiences. The wish appeals to the client's higher self.

Central to Psychophonetics is "'I am' awakening." What does this mean? Awakening to what? In the context of this book and its modality, it means awakening to the "I am," or one's core self, the inner spiritual spark, and to the "I am" in others. The central importance of awakening the "I am" is to become more conscious and available for transformation and healing. In this book processes are described that can support this awakening. Change and transformation within means bringing our awareness to situations, and becoming more conscious is also a practice in which awakening has many layers. Awakening the "I" also means we are participating in taking another step for humanity and the earth. This step is happening through the heart, and it is through the heart flow that we can develop a consciousness of soul, learn to cooperate harmoniously with others, and eventually uplift the consciousness of humanity.

This book is one contribution toward ways of creating conditions for shifts in consciousness. It is an introduction to the practice of Psychophonetics. The first three chapters give an outline of the background, theory and methodology of Psychophonetics psychotherapy, to provide the reader with an understanding of and orientation to this modality and as a basis for understanding the chapters in the second section of the book. Some sections in the first part have been adapted from my doctoral research thesis that focused on client experiences of change and transformation through Psychophonetics psychotherapy, as well as the writings of Yehuda Tagar.

In the second section, *Stories and Insights from Practice,* the chapters are by a number of practitioners to give the reader insight into this modality and its applications within the field of counseling and psychotherapy. In these chapters, each author discusses a topic or issue that is meaningful for them, bringing something special and unique that will, one hopes, inspire the reader.

Descriptions of the therapeutic process with clients are described and in a number of cases, the clients themselves have contributed and given their permission for their contributions to be included in this book with artwork, poetry, and comments. Having a variety of voices expressed in a range of ways gives a practical, in-depth and more authentic perspective on how this approach works in practice. However, direct experience is ultimately the only way to encounter the real potential and reality of this modality.

Psychophonetics has evolved out of the accumulated experience of developing and applying it in the field of counseling/psychotherapy. It recognizes that reality is the meaning that each person gives to his/her experience and if we can perceive our experience afresh, we are then freer to give it new meaning. The possibility of developing self-awareness through creative expression to observe our inner life actively allows us consciously to create new meaning. My deepest gratitude goes to Yehuda Tagar, the founder of Psychophonetics, who has developed a way and process for healing and transformation, as well as established a new vocation.

This work must bear fruit, and completing this book is a step in making Psychophonetics more known and available in the world. The year 2010 is an auspicious time for this book's publication, as it is one hundred years since Steiner gave the psychosophy lectures in 1910.

Robin Steele Ph.D.
Melbourne, Australia

Part 1

Psychophonetics Counseling/Psychotherapy

Chapter 1

Background and Introduction to Psychophonetics

Robin Steele

The nature and field of psychotherapy practice is very diverse, and it is estimated that there are about four hundred and fifty different types of psychotherapy approaches. This diversity has resulted in the establishment of a whole range of schools with their own theoretical approaches. However, beyond types of approaches, recognition of the client's perspective is becoming increasingly acknowledged as important, and that the client's perceptions of the counseling process are crucial in therapy, as they may differ from those of the counselor. Another aspect that is becoming more important for effective work with clients is that approaches toward thinking, feeling and doing need to be more integrated into the counselor's approach. Psychophonetics is one approach that considers these factors.

Background and Context

Psychophonetics is an expressive therapy that embraces a holistic view of the human being as a living body, soul, and spirit. It was developed in the 1980s by Yehuda Tagar and bases its theoretical and methodological roots in the spiritual work of Rudolf Steiner in Anthroposophy and psychosophy (Rudolf Steiner's lectures on psychology), as well as in humanistic psychology and the expressive arts. It is a phenomenological approach to human experience that facilitates a process of active exploration and self-discovery, that each person may become more conscious for healing and transformation in his/her relationships and way of being in the world.

Psychophonetics counseling and psychotherapy has similarities with the action therapies such as the expressive, experiential, and Gestalt therapies, but is unique with its philosophical foundation in Anthroposophy and psychosophy, its understanding of the human being as body, soul and spirit, and with its application of bodily awareness/ sensation, gesture, visualization and use of sound in therapy. It also differs in that each session combines both a person-centered conversational phase with an action phase that incorporates experiential, creative and expressive methods. The words *counseling* and *psychotherapy* are both applicable in this context and are used interchangeably throughout the book. Psychophonetics creates a bridge between approaches that operate mainly through the verbal dimension and those that operate mainly through expression, body awareness and the experiential dimension. It combines cognitive, experiential and behavioral aspects into the process, facilitated by the choice of the "I" or self, thereby having a transpersonal dimension.[1] With a verbal, conversational component and a nonverbal, expressive component in each session, the client can consciously integrate newly accessed experiential content.

From his personal, spiritual and artistic strivings,[2] Yehuda Tagar originally created Psychophonetics as a methodology of human experience. A biographical summary of those efforts are as follows. From his early twenties, Tagar wrote poetry and practiced Rudolf Steiner's seven conditions of spiritual development[3] as a path of ongoing personal development. From 1981 to 1984, after completing the Foundation Year in Anthroposophy at Emerson College at twenty-seven years old, Yehuda studied at the London School of Speech Formation, where he began

1 Tagar (2003).

2 Tagar (1996c)

3 Steiner (1994). See *How to Know Higher Worlds*, chapter 5, "Conditions for Spiritual Development."

working with dramatic theater as a path of awakening to the reality of human being-ness, based on Steiner's lectures in *Speech and Drama.*[4] It was also during this time that Yehuda began his studies in psychology at the Psychosynthesis Institute in London but then discovered and shifted his focus to Steiner's approach to psychology and psychosophy. At thirty-one years of age, in 1984, he wrote a founding paper on an alternative method of acting, based on Rudolf Steiner's suggestion of sound feelings (*Lautempfindung*) and sound sensing (*Lautstimmung*), which later became known as Philophonetics.[5]

This journey of working deeply with drama and the sounds of human speech led the thirty-two-year-old Yehuda to Australia in 1985 to study further with Mechthild Harkness, the founder of the Harkness Studio, a school of speech and drama in Sydney. In 1986, at thirty-three years old, he named his developing methodology of acting: firstly as Philophonetica, then as Philophonetics, which culminated in 1990 with Yehuda directing the play *Dr. Faustus* by Christopher Marlow, presented at La Mama Theatre in Adelaide.

Studies in humanistic, existential, and transpersonal counseling approaches to human development alongside the study of Steiner's Spiritual Science, the seven conditions, psychosophy, and Steiner's lectures on psychoanalysis,[6] led to a path of personal development, healing and transformation and to Yehuda forming a training college in counseling and psychotherapy. In summary, exploration of psychosophy and of Steiner's approach to drama was a laboratory for practical exploration, with psychosophy becoming the conceptual background and psychological language for the drama research, motivated and grounded by ongoing personal development. From these streams, Philophonetics formed as a path of exploring human experience, and as a method of

---

4 Steiner (2007a).

5 *Philophonetics* means "love of sounds," as awareness of one's experience through body awareness/sensing, movement, visualization and the sounds of human speech.

6 Steiner (1990). *Psychoanalysis and Spiritual Psychology.*

deep observation of the interactive dynamics of body, psyche, consciousness and spiritual awareness for the purpose of the performing arts, for a deepening of adult education and for the experiential study of Rudolf Steiner's Anthroposophy and psychosophy.

During the late 1980s, Philophonetics counseling evolved as an application of the Philophonetics methodology. In 1991, in response to requests, a training course was established, firstly in Adelaide and then primarily based in Melbourne until Yehuda moved to South Africa at ate forty-nine, where in 2003 it was renamed Psychophonetics. Since the mid-1990s, there has been a growing group of professional practitioners in Australia, South Africa and England who have completed the three-year professional training course in Psychophonetics and have worked or are working in such areas as hospitals, medical and health clinics, drug rehabilitation, research, schools, government organizations, business, and in private practice. Some practitioners have chosen to do further training to become a teacher and/or supervisor of Psychophonetics at Persephone Institute/College, while some have also gone on to develop personal development programs and workshops based on Psychophonetics and to complete further postgraduate research in this field at the university level.

This brief biographical background gives a sense of how this modality has evolved and developed since the 1980s. There are similarities in some areas with other approaches, for example, drama therapy uses theater techniques and a variety of interventions such as performances with actors and individual empty-chair role plays to create processes for dramatic distancing or story situations in which a person can identify with a particular character as a metaphor.[7] However, Psychophonetics has followed a different path of development, even though it has been influenced by drama principles. For instance, any *characters* experienced in a Psychophonetics session come from within the individual's own inner soul life, expressed through combinations of sensing, gesturing, visualization and sounds. The therapy session

7 Dramatherapy: http://en.wikipedia.org/wiki/Drama_therapy.

becomes an inner drama of inner characters, not as role play, but as real events from each person's inner soul experience in which distancing is an activity of *Beholding* whereby they can see their own inner characters and inner dynamics with perspective. Psychophonetics is working with the drama of each person's soul life and the client is actor and primary director.

Psychosophy: A Psychology of Soul

Many counseling issues today are concerned with difficulties relating to the consciousness soul,[8] to individual development and choices. With psychosophy being a psychology of the soul, this creates the possibility and conditions for personal development to become spiritual development. Psychosophy[9] is the name used by Rudolf Steiner for his primary lectures on psychology, as the study of the human soul between body and spirit and as a foundation for a future spiritual psychology, as a psychology of freedom.

A fundamental element of Anthroposophy is the threefold nature of the human being, and psychosophy is about bringing to consciousness the experiences of the soul in relation to body and spirit. Psychosophy describes how we can come to know the human soul by direct observation of self and others, experienced through the soul's inner life. In 1909, Rudolf Steiner brought a new understanding of child development in his book: *The Education of the Child in the Light of Anthroposophy.* Child psychology is a fundamental aspect of any psychology and these ideas became the basis of the curriculum we know as Waldorf (or Steiner) education.

---

8 In terms of the evolution of consciousness, the time of the consciousness soul is seen as the historical period in which we now live.

9 *Psychosophy* (study of the soul) was the term used by Rudolf Steiner in a course of lectures in Berlin, Nov. 1910. It was intended to be the foundation for anthroposophic (or spiritual) psychology, to be studied in context with two other courses, *Anthroposophy* (study of the human being) and *Pneumatosophy* (study of spirit), all of which are published together as *A Psychology of Body, Soul, and Spirit* (Steiner, 1999).

After giving the psychosophy lectures, Steiner continued to talk about the need for a psychology of soul, as he did in his lectures on psychoanalysis from 1912 to 1921[10] and especially in the range of lectures given in 1924,[11] in some of his final lectures before he died. At that time however, psychosophy was not taken up and developed. It is only in the last twenty to thirty years that psychosophy has gained more attention.[12]

When psychosophy is applied practically, it can become a path of soul transformation in which new organs of sense need to be created for soul observation. In his book *Anthroposophy (A Fragment),* Steiner (1996a) wrote about the human senses needed for the observation of external reality, and he described three more senses that need to be developed consciously in each person for observing the hidden reality of human existence: Imagination for *seeing* the invisible reality of life dynamics; Inspiration for *hearing* the inaudible dynamics of living souls; and Intuition for *knowing* spiritual beings from within.

The transformation of the higher sense organs of thinking, feeling, and willing into organs for Imagination, Inspiration, and Intuition require acts of self-transformation. Rudolf Steiner's guidance in esoteric training toward these three deeds of transformation disclose that the inner soul phenomena of fear, hate, and doubt, the "Three Beasts of the Abyss," must be encountered and, to a certain extent, be overcome for transformation of this kind to take place in the soul.

Psychophonetics is a form of applied psychosophy in that it works with the dynamics of the human soul. These dynamics are perception, thinking, feeling, willing and intuiting, with the "I" being the integrator of the soul dynamics. It is a methodology of phenomenological

10 Steiner's lectures about Freud and Jung in: *Psychoanalysis in the Light of Anthroposophy* (1990).

11 For example: Steiner's lectures to the priests and to the doctors; the karmic relationships lectures; speech and drama; education, eurythmy and others.

12 A current author on psychosophy well worth reading is William Bento, who wrote: *Lifting the Veil of Mental Illness: An Approach to Anthroposophical Psychology.*

observation of the human soul, and speaking from the soul through the language of experience. This includes developing an understanding of the elements and interacting forces of soul life; the nature of memory between the "I" and the etheric body; the three streams of soul life as coming from past, present and future; the process of how we digest experience; how mental pictures are stored in the etheric stream of the soul; and how using body awareness and expression offers a way for the "I am" to access memories into consciousness, enabling new perspectives and new meanings. Psychosophy provides a method for the study and transformation of human experience and the following chapters describe examples of how this is applied practically through Psychophonetics.

Psychophonetics accepts awareness through the living body as a way of knowing through bodily sensation, movement and gesture, visualization of internal dynamics, and the resonance of sound therapy. These modes of awareness of experience are nonverbal and pre-reflective, with the potential for understanding experience directly, with no distortions.[13] Psychophonetics can be described as a process of experience—awareness through intentionality, starting from the premise that experience is a real event happening in the human psyche or soul, leaving impressions or imprints that are stored in resonating patterns of sensory dynamics. These imprints of experience can be accessed through body awareness, sensing, gestures, visualization and sounds. The correlation between the imprints of sound experiences and the imprints of human experience in the bodily layers enables the method of sound naming used in Psychophonetics psychotherapy.[14]

Psychophonetics begins with the assumption that we are evolving, spiritual beings, and that problems are potentially an opportunity for growth. Counseling takes place within the context of the soul's development and from the perspective that there is a spiritual core of the human being, the "I" (or "I am"), as a conscious principle that we can

13 Tagar (2003).

14 Steele (2004).

come to know. This means a knowing that is "grounded in personal experience" and not "subservient to authority."[15] By staying close to direct experience, by being attentive firstly to bodily experience, and through a journey of questioning that embraces body, soul and spiritual knowledge, we can become more active in imaginal and intuitive thinking. From this, we can come to know in a real way rather than in an abstract way. Barry Bignell confirms this by saying, "Awareness of our true individuality, our 'I'-ness, is achieved by learning to observe, as it is happening, our own contribution to knowing, our intentionality, which, for Steiner, is synonymous with spiritual activity."[16]

Becoming attentive to oneself, and to soul, is a relatively new development that demands that we become more conscious in our daily lives. The position of the "I" in the soul is central to Psychophonetics. From being in the middle realm of soul, as the realm of experience, we can move up toward the spirit or dive down into the bodily layers of the subtle bodies (physical, etheric and astral). A sense of wholeness or integration is felt when the "I" is creating a sense of equilibrium or wellbeing in these layers of our being. But we need to stay alert to the fact that in our soul life everything is moving and changing and metamorphosing, where: "On the one side there is the force of desiring, through which the soul is embedded into the processes and functions of the organs of the living body; on the other side is the force of cognition, as the highest soul function, unfolding where the spirit penetrates the soul."[17]

Psychophonetics accepts that our "I am" consciousness can travel through the layers of our being consciously and unconsciously. This can affect our health and wellbeing. For instance, if the astral enters too much into the etheric layer and penetrates into the physical too much over a period of time, disease may manifest through an imbalance in the system. Or, if people become too "up in the air" or "out of their body," they can become more ungrounded and less present to the world around

15 Bignell (2000:494).

16 Bignell (2000:497).

17 Zeylmans van Emmichoven (1982:94).

them. Rudolf Treichler[18] says that physical illness arises when soul forces are too deeply embedded into the body, while in contrast he suggests that in an extreme case of insanity, the spirit has withdrawn completely.

Another way of looking at this idea is in relation to the different emphases in some modalities of psychotherapy. For example, in a very general sense, the somatic therapies may focus primarily on working with the physical body, while other therapies like psychoanalysis may focus more on the mind, while the experiential therapies such as Gestalt, Jungian and experiential therapies may focus primarily on soul experience. Perhaps this is becoming less true nowadays, as there is a growing trend across many schools of thought to become more integrated and inclusive of various approaches.

Having an awareness of our living body means being aware of the processes inherent in life that can influence how we process experiences. Steiner named these life processes breathing, warming, nourishing, secreting, maintaining, growing and generating,[19] and indicated how they can impact our health, life and wellbeing. Wellbeing could be described as a feeling of completeness, wholeness, integration, a coming together, being more present, balanced, attuned, flowing, that creates a sense of equilibrium unique in each person. Emotional issues could be seen as processes of addressing the disturbance of this balance. For instance, breathing, warming and nourishment can manifest in a sense of wellbeing, while a disturbance in breathing can be felt as anxiety; a disturbance in warmth can be felt as coldness; and a disturbance in

18 Treichler (1989:134).

19 Steiner (1996a). This book was written in 1910, the same year he gave the psychosophy lectures. These seven life processes are necessary for our development and can also become transformed into soul forces as an adult: Breathing-taking in/observing/perceiving; warming-relating/connecting/memory; nourishing- digesting/assimilating/self-care; secreting-sorting/individualizing/questioning; maintaining-practice/exercising; growing-developing faculties; reproducing-creating/forming. Another useful reference by Steiner on the life processes is: *The Riddle of Humanity*. For the soul learning processes see: van Houten (1995) *Awakening the Will*.

nourishment can be perceived as an emotional deprivation of needs in the various layers of the human being.

In this expressive and experiential therapeutic approach, issues can be addressed on all the bodily levels using the range of nonverbal skills as needed. These skills enable us to become more consciously aware of our experience, to become more oriented in thinking, more able to take action and be connected in our feeling life. Consequently, the life forces are stimulated to harmonize any disturbed emotional/psychological activities and to strengthen the integration of the "I am." A longitudinal research study on clients' experience of change through Psychophonetics psychotherapy sessions[20] focused on volunteer participant clients who had chosen to attend counseling. This research shows that there are different aspects in the process of change. One aspect was how clients changed over time through a number of phases connected with the life processes. These processes occur all the time, within a session, as well as over a longer period in the process of learning and changing and are always interweaving and overlapping within us, rather than happening sequentially. The process of therapeutic change incorporates our ability to digest our past, present and future experiences, through the following life/soul processes: taking in/perceiving; relating/connecting; assimilating/self-care; sorting out/individualizing; practicing/exercising new capacities; growing and developing new faculties; creating and forming something new in our lives.[21] Being aware of how these processes are working within us is important for conscious development.

The Body—Embodied Knowing

Psychophonetics combines counseling, artistic expression, body awareness and self-observation as part of the therapeutic process in which the client is the source of information, observation, choices,

---

20 Steele (2005).

21 More detailed information about these soul processes can be found in *Awakening the Will* and *Practicing Destiny* by Coenraad van Houten (1995) and in Robin Steele's Ph.D. research study (2005).

direction and action. Nonverbal communication is used as a way of going beyond the limitations of verbal expression to access feelings, emotions, reactive patterns, defenses and potentials embedded in the deep layers of the living body.

Body is not seen just as a physical body, but as an "ensouled" being. One way of describing the body is to see it as the mediator between the inner and the outer dimensions of human experience. Yehuda Tagar defines the human body as "a living instrument for personal experience and meaning, enabling an inner being (the psyche) to live in outer space (that is, the rest of the world)."[22] The dimensions of the human body can be seen as comprising various layers of being: a physical body, a life body, and a sentient–soul–astral body that enable the presence of the "I am," the self-aware, conscious, and individualized dimension of our being.

Human experience, according to Rudolf Steiner's model of the human being, is imprinted or registered in the subtle bodies that lie between the physical body and the mind, in the ether/life body and the astral body (the body of emotions, desires, feelings). It is here that memories of experience live: "an invisible reality" made up of "processes, rhythms and formative forces."[23]

What is meant by these dimensions of bodily life? To summarize, we can say that the physical body is the form, the skeleton—the earth element in us; the life/etheric body is the movement, fluids and life processes—the water element in us; the sentient or astral body is the inner experience, inner life, sensing, desiring, instincts—the air element in us; and the "I am" consciousness is being awake, the self-aware and reflective level of existence, present in the blood—the warmth or fire element in us.[24] The "I am" consciousness can connect us with the transpersonal and transcendent aspects of spirit, and can also be referred to as the "Self," our unique individual essence. Our bodily layers develop as we grow into adulthood, and throughout our life we continue to work through these layers with

22 Tagar (1993:34).

23 Tagar (1995:22).

24 Steiner (1996).

inner forces of soul and spirit. This relationship between the physical, life and astral bodies, and the "I am" is described by Rudolf Steiner:

> The physical body would fall apart if the ether body did not hold it together. The ether body would sink into unconsciousness if the astral body did not illumine it. Likewise, the astral body would repeatedly forget the past if the "I" did not rescue this past and carry it over into the present. What *death* is to the physical body and *sleep* to the ether body, *forgetting* is to the astral body. We can also say that life belongs to the ether body, consciousness to the astral body, and memory to the "I."[25]

The human body's role in consciousness can be seen as simultaneously being an absorber, a carrier, a reflector, an expresser and a transformer of experience.[26] The body is important not only as the mediator between the inner and the outer dimensions of experience but also as a valuable source of knowledge, as embodied knowing. Working with the body and soul processes and accessing imagination makes thinking alive.

As a holistic approach, this means Psychophonetics includes the whole human being as body, soul, and spirit, and when counselors try to separate or grasp at something as an object or give power to some fixed idea, they will find that their work with clients probably will not flow and that imagination is diminished. This work requires thinking that is flexible and uses imagination. Therefore, practitioners have to stay alert to how they are thinking, as well as to how they are feeling and behaving.

This means remaining flexible, balanced and alert enough in thinking so as not to be caught in a flight of ideas in which no forms can be created, or not to become too determined in a fixed idea without being able to develop further possibilities. It is an unsettling way of being that encourages a *living* form of thinking, of awareness and consciousness that is not a denial of the intellect or a way toward just feelings and imagining. Clinical experience and research show that, when we are thinking

25 Steiner (1997), pp. 39–40.

26 Tagar (1993).

consciously and authentically, participating in a living way, something new can arrive and a unity is present, with its own internal logic.

How we interpret an event and the meaning we give it is important. This means healing lies, not in searching for the cause and effect, but in our power to change what an experience means to us. Understanding causality, in the holistic mode of consciousness, is a complex matter, and it is worth reading Henri Bortoft's book, *The Wholeness of Nature: Goethe's Way of Science,* in which he explores how a new understanding of causality can be seen as "dynamic simultaneity."[27] The Psychophonetics practitioner is mindful not to think in a causal way about the connections between emotions and body but to hold a more embodied and holistic connection of body, soul, mind and spirit, which is becoming more accepted in the growing field of body–soul–spirit and in the related field of psychoneuroimmunology.

The body can become a map for the landscape of our experience. With this body map, psychosomatic issues are accessible when specific experiences are felt in the physical body with no obvious physical cause, as an inherent connection exists in the dynamics of emotion and motion, in that: "every emotion is a motion in reserve; every motion, an externalized emotion."[28] This idea is also described in various other body-oriented and artistic therapies, such as bioenergetics, Gestalt, and art and movement therapies. When motion is held back, meaning and/or memory is held in the body, in the bodily tensions and gestures, until they are released.

The memory of our life experiences is being stored within the vibrating, resonating life body of sounds. Current life experiences of a similar nature can trigger these memories and affect the resonance of the life body, affecting the soul life. That is, the activity of the life body, as well as stored experiences, influence the soul functions of thinking, feeling and willing.

27 Henri Bortoft (1996:339).

28 Tagar (1993:41).

Psychophonetics is an embodied and expressive way of knowing, with forms of knowledge that are less visible than cognitive forms of knowledge. In Psychophonetics, clients are encouraged to connect with their experience through *sensing*, then to extend this process using gesture, visualization and sounds. For example, sensing and gesturing the experience of a knotted feeling in the stomach may bring up layers of anger or sadness with an insight into this that brings a shift in consciousness, and through invoking and connecting with the inner qualities needed, healing can occur.

A belief in the body's wisdom is at the heart of Psychophonetics, in which there is a trust in the knowing and in the truth that comes through body and soul into conscious awareness. Faculties of self-knowledge through direct experience can be developed by engaging in a conscious soul relationship with experience through body awareness, sensing, movement, visualization and the sounds of human speech, as well as with verbal communication.[29] These four major modes of knowing comprise the *literacy of experience* that will be described further in chapter two.

Basic Ethical Principles of Psychophonetics— a Psychosophical Approach

Based on years of practical research into Anthroposophy, psychosophy, and various counseling approaches, a number of ethical principles have been developed that give a spiritual context and attitude for the practice of this modality.[30] The following is a summary of these principles.[31]

29 Tagar (1995).

30 The theoretical and philosophical background for these principles can be found in these writings by Rudolf Steiner: *Goethe's Theory of Knowledge*; *Intuitive Thinking as a Spiritual Path; How to Know Higher Worlds; Theosophy*, and in his lectures: *A Psychology of Body, Soul, and Spirit; Education for Special Needs; Transforming the Soul* (2 vols.); and *The Foundations of Human Experience.*

31 These principles were developed and written by Yehuda Tagar and are taught as the basic principles for being a Psychophonetics therapist. The

Inner equipment—Each person's life, with its challenges and crises, is considered to be an opportunity for learning and development. Learning to digest experience is a way of forging each person's inner capacities and applying these to the developmental process. The essential assumption is that the resources for the next step in each person's development, healing and transformation are potentially available within his/her inner life and outer circumstances. This connection can create a shift in a person's inner resources and life circumstances, encouraged by the practitioner.

Inner guidance—The counseling process provides opportunities and safeguards for the individual's potential internal guidance to be consciously present. The counselor's personal, professional, and philosophical knowledge and experience do not take the place of the client's inner guidance. The final answer to such questions as: what are the main issues to deal with at any given point in time; what should be the direction or goals of the session; how intense, confrontational, nurturing or otherwise must come from the client. Each session is conducted in such a way as to ensure that there is the opportunity for the client to make these choices and to give direction in the process.

Self-knowledge—The client is the one who knows the meaning of his/her experience. Psychophonetics sees meaning as a creation of the human spirit, so the counselor's role is to create opportunities for self-observation, stimulate new perspectives and encourage fresh thinking for new meaning. Clients are the knowers, interpreters, bearers of the meaning of their own experiences, and the role of the counselor is to encourage this knowing.

Teamwork—The role of the counselor could be described as an encouraging companion in the journey of the client's quest for self-knowing. That companionship is expressed through cooperative activity, with the counselor's position as co-knowing, co-seeing, and co-

---

full, detailed version is available from the professional association of Psychophonetics practitioners (IAPP).

supporting aspects of the client's inner life being focused on. *The client is considered an active member of the therapeutic team.* An important motto for this teamwork is, "Where two or three are gathered together in my name, then there 'I am' in the midst of you." The "I am" is understood here as the "universal human" consciousness manifesting through the "I am" of each person present. For the development of the consciousness soul, people have to learn to take their own authority, which means that teamwork is important.[32]

The "I am" (the client's "I am" or core self) is given every possible opportunity to be fully present in the process, to guide, to make choices, and to know. This principle governs all professional choices in the therapy process. In the anthroposophic model of the human constitution, the "I" is the integrative center of the human psyche, our core identity. The "I" is the observer, the feeler, the meaning maker, and choice maker in regards to our own experience, as well as in regard to meeting experiences that come to us in the world. The Psychophonetics process could be described as allowing, inviting, enabling, facilitating and encouraging the clients' "I am" to enter every aspect of their experience. The main practical activities include consciously experiencing, focusing, sensing, gesturing, visualizing, speaking, moving, expressing creatively, sounding, naming, beholding/observing, making choices, sharing. Applying this principle helps to prevent any dependency issues between client and practitioner.

Higher accountability—This principle is a striving in which there is an ongoing readiness for practitioners to question their own view on reality, rather than imposing an interpretation. Striving for a higher accountability is a commitment to review our own psychological dynamics and our personality from the standpoint of our innermost spirituality, in the context of each person's culture and including the *universal human* dimension.

A path of self-development—The practitioners regularly review and reflect on their practice, personally and professionally, through

32 Tagar (1995a).

supervision.[33] An ongoing inner development means attending to the following seven conditions:[34]

1. Striving to develop a healthy body and soul by *maintaining self-care* on all levels (physical, emotional, energetic, spiritual).
2. Feeling connected with all of existence; to recognize we are in everything and everything is in us; not to judge others but be able to stand in their shoes—*developing empathy.*
3. Recognizing that our thoughts and feelings have as much significant influence as our deeds, and that work on our inner life is as important as work on our outer life—*acknowledging internal dynamics.*
4. Recognizing that the true essence of a human being does not lie in a person's outer appearance, but rather in his/her inner nature, in the soul and spiritual existence of that person. Finding a genuine balance between having an open heart for the demands of the outer world and maintaining inner strength and "unshakeable endurance"—*identity and boundaries.*
5. The ability to be true to a decision once made, even in the face of daunting adversity, until we come to the conclusion that it was or is made in error—*acting on resolutions.*
6. Developing thankfulness for everything that meets us, and the universal love that allows the world to reveal itself fully to us—*gratitude and appreciation.*
7. *Inner consistency* of character and equanimity with the previous six conditions.

Psychophonetics was founded on the basis of working with these conditions as a pathway for balanced adult development as they create

33 For example, in an article about counseling a client about his or her jealousy, Tagar (1994a) describes how this prompted the need for his own inner work around jealousy.

34 These seven conditions are described by Rudolf Steiner in chapter 5, "Conditions for Spiritual Development," in his book *How to Know Higher Worlds* (1994). They are the basic conditions for the inner development and training of Psychophonetics practitioners.

a systematic approach for enhancing wellbeing and manifesting inner potential, for personal and professional growth and creativity.

The above principles embrace the practical applications of the basic ethics and philosophy underlying Psychophonetics. They reflect, within the practical steps of the counseling and group processes, its attitude toward human potential, dignity and freedom, in which each person can learn to see his/her life as an ongoing and unfolding process or journey that has inherent wisdom.

Based on this background, we will now enter the next chapter to learn more about how psychosophy is applied in practice through the nonverbal modes of knowing and the aspects of experience awareness, including the unique applications of sound in therapy.

Chapter 2

Awakening to Human Experience

Robin Steele

The Literacy of Experience

A basic operational definition of experience can be described as, "Everything that reaches my awareness from outside of that awareness."[1] The role of the Psychophonetics practitioner is to expand the experiential field of consciousness through the body, for self-exploration and to expand awareness into the given dynamics of experience, to integrate this into personal knowledge. Sound work provided the major tool for exploring experience in the creation of Philophonetics and Psychophonetics, and the combination of the four nonverbal modes of knowing—sensing, gesture, visualization and sounds—form the *literacy of experience.*

Psychosophy strives to make conscious our soul experiences in relation to the physical world of the senses, to the spiritual world as it appears through the core of our being, and to the soul world as experienced through our own inner life. Human experience is experienced by the presence of the "I" and comes from three areas: from the outer world—perceived directly as sense impressions or as an echo of people or an event in the soul; from the body—mostly through bodily sensations and impulses; and from our inner life—through memories, images, reactions, thinking, feeling, instincts, actions, and so on.

---

1 Tagar (1999:247). This definition has been developed from Tagar's practical research, based on Rudolf Steiner's approach to cognition and psychology. For example, refer to Rudolf Steiner (2008) *Goethe's Theory of Knowledge: An Outline of the Epistemology of His Worldview.*

Awakening to the awareness of our experience means becoming conscious of how we can project our un-owned experiences and how we can color our perceptions with imprints from the past. In becoming more conscious, we need to be able to reexperience the inner layers of the absorbed experience, to reflect upon it, so we can create a new perspective. Experiences stored in the vibrational dynamics of our life body may be accessed into our awareness consciously or remembered spontaneously; or they may remain not in our consciousness but only trigger reactions and color our perceptions and feelings. These dynamics are accessible to bodily sensation. We can sense the movements, shapes and vibrations of these imprints in our soul and they become accessible through the activities of gesturing, visualizing and sound.

Summary of the Four Modes of Knowing

Sensing or sensory intelligence leads us into the exploration of the dynamics of experience registered in the life body as the first step in observing and bringing into conscious awareness the phenomenon being explored. Expressing experience through bodily *gestures and movement* is a kinesthetic mode of knowing, which accesses our intuitive intelligence. Gestures and movement can stimulate spontaneous *visualizations*, as a pictorial mode of knowing, activating our imaginative intelligence, in which we form inner images that pictorially express inner experiences. The fourth mode of knowing is *sound intelligence*. It is the echo of human experience through the sounding of the consonants and vowels of human speech. This is accessed through the identification of the vibrational nature of each aspect of experience and the ability to resonate with its inner nature through sounding. In Psychophonetics, these experiences, seen as living in the form of vibrations within us, can be traced, accessed, released and enhanced by matching them with a sound or sound combinations that have a sympathetic resonance with them. Sound therapy is a major tool for directly accessing and addressing the deepest layers of human experience.[2] The following is a more detailed description of each mode:[3]

Sensing: The sentient mode of knowing is the human sense ability that receives and retains impressions from the outer and inner worlds. Every experience leaves an imprint on us, taken in through the bodily processes into our soul life where it continues to live. Through the senses (Steiner describes twelve senses), we can rediscover and bring into conscious awareness at any point in time a particular experience and become aware of its related psychological processes. Some senses are directed to outer perceptions, some to inner perceptions, and some to the perception of meaning. These senses relate more to a general functioning of the body that overrides organ division, for instance, like the sense of touch.

Sensing out relates to sight, hearing, smell, taste, touch and warmth; *sensing in* relates to sense of life (wellbeing), sense of balance and sense of movement; *sensing meaning* (in and out) relates to sense of intonation (of sound, word, speech), sense of concept (grasping the meaning of others' expressed words), and sense of "I" (sensing the presence of another human being). We can group these senses further according to body, soul and spirit: body—inner senses of touch, life, movement and balance, relates the activity of doing/willing; soul—inner/outer senses of smell, taste, sight and warmth, relates to our feeling life; and spirit—outer senses of hearing, speech, concept, and the "I" of the other, relates to the activity of thinking.[4]

The dynamics of experience can become observable and accessible for change and healing through body awareness by focusing on the sensation in the body. Every emotional experience can be traced to

---

2 More details about the nature and therapeutic application of sounds can be found in articles by Steele (2004) and Tagar (2003).

3 Tagar (1991, 1994, 1996, 2003), Sherwood & Tagar (2000).

4 For further study of the senses, read Steiner's books on the topic, (1979) *The World of the Senses and the World of the Spirit*, and (1981) *Man as a Being of Sense and Perception*. Albert Soesman's book is also useful: (1998) *Our Twelve Senses: Wellsprings of the Soul*.

its origin by the vibrations in the subtle dynamics of the body and by using gesture—movement that can directly express the sensations.

Gesturing/Movement: The kinesthetic mode of knowing is the expression of experience through bodily gestures and movement. Gesture and movement enhance the imaginative ability inherent in everyone to create precise mental pictures that can reveal the inner psychosomatic dynamics being explored. In Psychophonetics, the human body is regarded as "an instrument of meaning, enabling an inner being to live in an outer world."[5] In this sense, the body serves as a map for the psyche through which we can consciously trace and observe our inner life.

Visualizing: The mental/pictorial mode of knowing is the formation of inner images that pictorially represent inner experiences. Human experience can be transformed into and retained in pictorial representations and can be recalled, explored, expressed visually and transformed. Spontaneous visualizations arising from a gesture that is expressed and physically exited from become powerful, reliable modes of knowing.

Sounding: The mental/audible mode of knowing is the echo of human experience through the sounding of the consonants and vowels of human speech. For example, a sensation of a headache, shoulder tightness, knotted stomach, pained neck can be sensed and expressed through clenching the fists, contorting the whole body and, with the help of holding the breath, then releasing it with sounds that arise, are found directly relating to the specific experience (for example, *GGah*, *Pshh*, *Dah*, *Bah*, *FFah . . .*).

Releasing makes it possible for the client to trace the origin of these tensions through the range of imaginative pictures that emerge, enabling exploration, encounter and release of deeper layers and patterns of response that cause the tensions. Finally, inner needs can be accessed, acknowledged, taken care of and healed by providing, invok-

5 Tagar (1999:249).

ing or nurturing the inner qualities needed, using movement and sounds that match the specific experience.

The Unique Application of Sounds in Therapy

I want to elaborate a little further on the topic of sounds, since they are a key element in Psychophonetics. The sounds of human speech are the foundation of all languages—about thirty-five to forty of them[6]—plus their combinations, which can affect us on all levels—physical, emotional, mental and spiritual. These *sounds of the psyche* are the sounds of human speech, consonants, vowels, their combinations and intonations—the alphabet. Sound therapy can touch us deeply:

> When all the sounds of human speech resound around a living human body, every aspect of one's inner experience, from every phase and level of one's life echoes and vibrates with them, like the strings of a piano with the sound of guitar strings nearby. Our subtle bodies, etheric and astral, are like the resonance chamber of the sounds.... The sounds are the hidden language of our inner life.[7]

This means the sounds of speech can play a significant role as they are interwoven within the layers of experience from our whole life and potentially provide the practitioner direct access to the depth of human experience. The vocabulary of sounds does not include words but sound formations, intonations, characters, coloring and shaping of the expressions of single sounds. Tagar sees the sounds as: "the deepest, most powerful mode of operation of our body of life and its forces"[8] and concludes from his observation and experience:

> The sounds of human speech, consonants and vowels, when spoken on their own, transform in the air into forms of vibrations that can echo in the whole range of human experience. Experiences live in the embodied layers of the psyche apparently exist in forms of

6 Steiner (2007a).

7 Tagar (1995:22).

8 Tagar (1997:173).

> vibrations similar to the vibrations of the sounds of speech... Every human experience, once expressed in a gesture, can find its precise counterpart in a particular combination of sounds of speech—sensed, spoken or visualized.[9]

The sounds can give each person a range of tools for exploration, expression and communication, for change and improvement in the inner life. Sound therapy, in this context, is done in a phenomenological way, from a position of not knowing and exploring experience as it presents itself in that moment, so the freedom and uniqueness of each person's experience is honored and respected, allowing the client to create new meaning.

The substance of the subtle body is made of sound vibrations and in these formative dynamics memory is stored.[10] The connection between the imprints of sound experiences and the imprints of human experience enables the *sound-naming* process used in the therapeutic sessions by Psychophonetics practitioners. Working with sounds is an ongoing development for the practitioner and one way of understanding sounds is through the basic elements. Yehuda Tagar developed this method of study as a guide for the practice of sound naming in the therapeutic context. The following basic alphabet is culturally biased to the sounds we are most familiar with and the reader is most welcome to add other sounds from other experiences and cultures.

When experimenting with sounds by saying them aloud and continuing or extending them, we can come into contact with each one's elemental characteristic. Even though the following sounds are classified into the elements, each sound can also be spoken in an earthy, watery, fiery or airy way. The following descriptions show the connection between the characteristics of the elements and their corresponding groups of sounds in their essence.[11]

---

9 Tagar (2003:99).

10 Refer to Steiner's lectures on psychosophy.

11 Tagar (1997:167–181) describes the nature of sounds in *Cooperating with the Life Forces from Within*. See also Steiner, *Eurythmy Therapy* (2009)

Earth element: G, K, D, T, B, P (the plosives). In speaking and allowing the body to move and gesture as we speak each of these sounds, we may experience how they create solid-like shapes in the air and our imagination can capture the form in pictures. A pain in the body may be experienced as a block and can be expressed and released with an earth sound. When the right sound is found to match that experience, it can bring a release in the flow of the life forces.

Wood element: Ng, N, M (the nasals). The nasals are the vibration of the wood element, between water and earth. These sounds can have the qualities of nurturing, wrapping and protecting, creating a protective sheath. They support the restoration of the protective functions of the body and in the psyche. In this way, nurturing can be rediscovered on the inner levels.

Water element: L, W. With these sounds, solids can be liquefied and blocks can be dissolved. Through the sounding of "L" and "W," we can trace and enhance the flow of liquids in our body and the flow of emotions in our psyche.

Air element: R1, R2, R3, R4 (said in four different ways—Scottish, English, French or African accent). All sounds can be spoken in an airy, breathy, free-flowing way, but the "R" sound expresses the vibrational nature of the air element in its very being. When we speak the "R" sound, we can observe how our whole body participates in the activity and how everything shakes, from stationary to vibrational. "R" can be used for revitalizing, energizing, detoxifying and echoing the same within the life body.

Fire element: H, S, Sh, Z, Th, Ch, F, V (the fricatives). Healing is based on warmth and warmth is expressed through the fire sounds. When the fire sounds are spoken energetically for a few minutes, the body will start to perspire. Warmth in the body can be depicted, imitated, enhanced, released, recreated and transformed through the power of the fire sounds.

---

and *Speech and Drama* (2007a) as the source for this work with sounds.

Light element: All the vowels (16) A (*ah*), E (*eh*), I (*ee*), O (*oh*), U (*oo*), Ä, Ö, Ü and the diphthongs A-I (*ai, ah-ee*), A-U (*ao, ah-oo*) and O-I (*oi, oh-ee*), U-I (*ui, oo-ee*) and reversed. Our bodies radiate light as a manifestation of the way our soul lives in the body. The light element is directly expressed in the vowels: *Ah* opens to the light, *U(oo)* closes from it; *O* embraces, encloses and protects while *I(ee)* pierces through, releases and brightens, *Eh* confronts, separates and awakens. Our moods can be expressed in vowel combinations and the most subtle differentiation of the flow of life can be depicted, diagnosed and enhanced with them. Sounding the vowels, either by expressing or sensing them on their own, or in combination with consonants, can transform an inner configuration of the life forces into a desired inner state.

The sounds ch, q, x, y, and z are not referred to because they are a combination of other sounds (for example: q = k & w). In addition, there is also the sound/chemical element and the element of meaning, and I refer the reader to the paper "Cooperating with the Life Forces"[12] for further reading about this. I will just say that inner experience and meaning can be communicated through the sounds and through the intonation of the sounds of human speech. For the Psychophonetics practitioner in particular, the intonation of the client's speech is the beginning of understanding the communication process, on which the rest of the therapeutic process is based. Rudolf Steiner[13] describes six main intonations of speech as expressions of sympathy, rejecting in a mood of antipathy, withdrawing into oneself, of feeling forward in the face of hindrances (hesitancy), effectiveness, and thoughtful expression. Psychophonetics also includes the mood of despair as a more recent characteristic. These shades of expression communicate the meaning in the sounds.

Sounds can perform a variety of functions, and in the therapeutic context, they can be useful for expressing inner experience, releasing inner blocks, for nurturing and transforming experiences. For instance, sounds that are useful for specific types of release and sometimes for

12 Tagar (1997:167-181).

13 Steiner (2007a).

naming certain types of attacking inner forces are the fricatives/explosive and steam-releasing sounds. These are made by combining an earth sound with a fire sound, with no vowel sound: For example, G-H; K-Ssss; T-Ch;T-Ssss; D-J; P-Fff; P-S; P-Sh.

If we explore each sound, we will find they have a unique quality or characteristic. Speaking single sounds creates a particular shape of airflow through the mouth and nose that can be traced through joining this airflow with hand movements. The following are some of the typical inner and outer expressions and responses that can occur while experiencing the sounds said aloud and expressed with the whole body:[14] *A (ah)*—opening, wonder; *U (oo)*—narrowing, deepening; *K*—breaking through a barrier, cutting; *MMM*—nurturing; *T*—pointing, incarnating; *D*—consolidating; *G*—guarding, fending off; and *B*—embracing, holding movement. Although there can be a commonality of experience with each sound, there are also individual differences in the experience of the sounds and in sound combinations. Sounds have shapes, movement and direction and these shapes are made by experiences in the subtle bodies that echo with the shapes created in us in response to the sounds.

In many healing traditions, the life body (etheric, chi or prana) is seen as a sphere of energy in constant motion. Sickness is considered to be movement that is blocked, while healing involves the release of blocked energy into movement. Therefore, sound naming the movement is as important as sound naming the form. Some examples of types of movement are: heavy/light; fast/slow; contraction/expansion; inward/outward; straight/round. These movements and sounds also have a specific direction, for example, upward, downward, pulling, pushing, from behind, from the front.[15]

For the practitioner, the skill of sound naming is to find the compatible sound that creates the same specific shape of the already created and imprinted experience. For instance, the shape could be

14 These descriptions of the Psychophonetics work with sounds, are written in chapter 21 of *Universal Sound*, by Crowley and Crowley (1994:289).

15 Tagar (1999a).

closed/open, straight/curvy, hard/soft, imploding/exploding, etc. Sounds also create forms and disperse them, allowing or preventing movement. Sounds are most effective when they arise organically out of breathing fully into a gesture of a particular experience, while moving physically with the whole body and sounding aloud. In the counseling session, the particular sounds applicable for each person emerge as unique expressions of an individual's specific soul experience in that particular time and place. The sounds will mean different things to different people according to their own experiences. The practitioner needs to take the following two principles into account when sound naming with a client. Only the person who is in the act of perceiving can be the one who knows the final sound for his/her experience. The practitioner may suggest possibilities to experiment with to expand the sound options, but only the clients can finally name the sound that matches their experience exactly. The other principle is that in order to find the sound for the experience, and for practitioners to help find it practically, they need to be in the position of being the *speaker* of the sound: "Only from the Speaking position can one actually conceive the sound, which is true Sound-Naming. From every other position one can only speculate the sound, not know it."[16]

Through body awareness, gesture and visualization, the sounds can address and enhance the bodily memory of experience and access untapped inner resources. The capacity of sounds to resonate with specific imprints of experience makes them a powerful therapeutic tool as they can echo the experience of invasion, of inner and outer pressures, impositions, abuse and criticism, as well as the experiences of protection, pain, release, nurturing and all aspects of desired inner strength. Sound therapy in combination with the other nonverbal modes is also effective for the practice of creating a space in which to be present, as well as in one's own authority, speaking, and expression. The following example describes a client's experience of using sound in a therapy session:

16 Tagar (1999a:8).

> On this particular day there was a difference in my nurturing as my heart was first covered in a woven blanket of love and warmth, which was pink and gold, and this then replaced with a pure gold blanket and it was ultra fine ...The sound (I sounded) was a warm high vibrating energy "MMMMMM" sound, with a central point to it but also vibrating graduating out, that was very nice and then after a couple of days of nurturing my heart, this beautiful pink color surrounded by exquisite perfumed rose petals, I could visualize and smell the petals...Until the heart had actually been healed and been given these nurturing sounds and the love that it required it couldn't experience joy. The sounds made a big change for me.

In summary, each experience can be traced, expressed and communicated through the basis language of the *literacy of experience.* Its position in relation to our awareness can be determined through the process of *experience awareness* and a sound or sounds combination can be found to match this experience through the Psychophonetics process of *sound naming.* This means matching a specific experience with a sound that resonates exactly with that experience, allowing the client an effective form of expression and a tool for further conscious exploration and healing.[17]

Awakening through the Life Processes

In his book *Anthroposophy (A Fragment),*[18] Rudolf Steiner takes the first steps toward developing a spiritual psychology. These fragmentary notes (written in 1910) became a basis for their psychosophy lectures given later that same year. This book includes descriptions of the senses, the life processes, the "I" experience and the relationship to the spiritual world. The life processes already mentioned in chapter one are: breathing, warming, nourishing, secreting, maintaining, growing and generating. Every experience in the life body is related to one or another of the seven life processes, which are unconscious etheric processes within us. From the therapeutic perspective, the life processes

---

17 Tagar (2003).

18 Steiner (1996a).

and our senses have a close relationship and "the life processes are a hidden dynamic that is missing in psychology, as sense impressions are experienced through the medium of the life processes which midwife the relationship between substance, soul and sense perception."[19] Our life of will lives organically through the life processes, and through them we internalize sense perceptions into our own being as a percept, as a memory picture and then as an idea to which we can give meaning. Our life processes mediate the integration of our sense perception and if there is a problem of the senses, then we also have a problem with the life processes.

This has important implications in the counseling context. It involves how clients perceive and take in sense impressions; how they digest their experiences; how well they can discriminate the essential from the nonessential and be motivated to change and connected to the deepest aspects of the self; and how intent and committed they are to allowing the new to emerge through practicing new faculties, growing new capacities and being able to embody and create something new in their lives.

From the counselor's perspective: How do we prepare before and as the client enters the room to sit down? We need to first sense and open up a space for something to happen in the session, which means breathing in a way that is about opening and differentiating between inner and outer, between expansion and contraction. Then we have to fill this space with an atmosphere of warmth and welcoming if we are going to create a safe relational space for the client to open up and be able to digest what is happening in the session. We can check this by asking if our room feels warm, hot, overheated or too cold. If our task has to do with transforming sensory impressions from the world through warmth and "I" consciousness, then it is important we understand how the life processes ensoul the senses, and travel through the etheric and astral layers to the "I."

19 This comment was made by Dr. James Dyson M.D. during a seminar I attended in 2010, in which he brought the medical and psychological perspectives together.

The counselor has another way of listening to the client when the life processes are considered, as they can affect the bodily, soul and spiritual layers of our being. One way of understanding this is through the metaphoric nature of certain words and polarities, which can describe how we are on the physical, etheric, astral, soul, relationship and spiritual levels of being. Note some examples of the types of words that clients may use: warm–cold, light–dark, contracted–expansive, open–closed, stuck–flowing, soft–hard, alive–dead, and many others.

The seven life processes in the context of the psychosomatic connection give the Psychophonetics counselor, who has this anthroposophic perspective, a rich source of language to name, observe, trace and make conscious these connections, and for the communication of imaginative pictures. This means that pain, for instance, may be a messenger of meaning. One client was feeling *stuck* and *hardened* in her body, preventing her from developing herself and her life. She said,, "I know that the disease I have had for the last few years, is emotion manifest in turning myself to stone so that I could protect myself and not feel physically or emotionally anymore, and that if I kept the negative energy in my body I would still remain sick.... Energy flows through your body and to keep it in there is detrimental to the body."

I worked professionally for many years in a complementary medical clinic with a number of doctors and health practitioners addressing physical and psychosomatic conditions. For example, clients experiencing the following conditions expressed positive results: Candida, cancer, MS; panic attacks, chronic pain, headaches and migraines, skin conditions, menstrual conditions, endometriosis, breathing and circulatory problems, stress and other general psychosomatic conditions. In many of these cases, healing occurs not by searching for the cause and effect, but from our power to change what an experience means to us.

By being in touch with our inner world of being and the outer world of the sense impressions and linking both, we can become our authentic selves in the world. To develop a healthy inner life we need to move beyond the world of the senses and be more in touch with a higher level through life/soul and spiritual experiences.

A client was fighting a disease and hating it until she decided to see a spiritual counselor, which changed everything. She realized that the disease was also a gift, in that it brought her attention to her body—allowing her to experience pain, to experience suffering in the body, to meet people and be exposed to different things. It allowed her to learn things about herself that she would never have known otherwise. She said, "That in itself was the beginning of being able to heal." Through the therapy, the life processes, especially breathing, warming and nourishing, combined with the bodily senses and her choices, had an important influence on the development of the disease. This process changed her energetically and physically. For instance, in this client's condition, there was a tendency toward contraction, stillness and coldness, which manifested as hardening (scleroderma), formation of calcium deposits around the skin and body and a resulting tightening and stiffness inside and outside of the body. Through the therapeutic process, she learned to bring in more breathing, movement and warmth, to create more rhythm in her life, so that softness began to replace hardness:

> My hands are like arthritics hand; my fingers don't straighten up, my wrists don't move, my skin is tight and hard as if the bone were just there. I do have fecal incontinence. I am still working on that one. Being on my own has given me that chance to heal without compromising. It has been my most important thing to do. And the fire is now stoked and keeping the warmth in my body and the love circulating through it which will in turn diffuse the disease.[20]

The life processes interpenetrate our life in complex ways and when taken in conjunction each of the seven conditions for personal and spiritual development, mentioned in chapter one, become a powerful path for personal and spiritual development, for developing an open mind, open heart and open will.

20 The description about this client comes from a PhD research study (Steele, 2005:163).

Aspects of Experience Awareness

The Philophonetics sounds laboratory was the origin of the methodology of experience awareness that then became the basis of Psychophonetics psychotherapy as a way of "tracing various aspects of experience and intentional deeds of the human 'I.'"[21] Psychophonetics practitioners are trained to be attentive to experience and to differentiate how they are actually responding to a particular experience. The skill of knowing where the "I" is in relation to an experience and where the clients' "I" is in relation to their experience is an important part of the practitioner's capacity to work with a client in a phenomenological way. The methodology of *experience awareness* was developed during the 1980s by Yehuda Tagar, through many years of experiential, phenomenological and practical laboratory research work on the sounds of human speech, which became a way of understanding human experience. The following are its main aspects:

Sensing: *I am encountering the experience.* Sensing is one of the major activities in the process of how we become more consciously aware through the body, as sensing bridges the "I" and the world. The process of sensing is when an outer or inner phenomenon reaches my consciousness, is registered as a sense impression and becomes an inner experience. That is, I perceive an event, I sense the impact of this event, and I can identify the relationship, boundaries and impact between "ME" and "IT" in the experience.[22]

Our ability to sense consists of more than just five senses; we are multisensory beings, and in the early 1900s, Rudolf Steiner wrote that we experience and become conscious through twelve senses. These twelve senses are like doorways through which we can come to know our self as an "I," to become oriented on the physical level; to be able to feel and develop relationships with the world, as soul; and to come to an inner understanding of other individuals. The senses of touch, life

21 Persephone College Resource material (1993a).

22 Tagar (1994).

(wellbeing), self-movement and balance are inner senses that give us awareness of ourselves as physical beings and provide a boundary condition between the soul life and the external world. The senses of smell, taste, sight and warmth are soul/feeling senses; and the four spiritual senses are sense of hearing, sense of sound/word (meaning intonation), sense of concept (the grasping of), and the sense of the "I" of another.[23] An experience of wholeness is felt through the life sense, which gives our sense of inner balance or equilibrium.

Some examples of sensing include: "I can sense tension in my shoulders. I can sense warmth in my heart. I can sense a presence of someone else in the room. I can smell lavender. I can taste the vegemite I ate earlier." A deeper study of the twelve senses can give us a greater imagination of the body in its dynamic, interactive relationship with the world and with how we experience the world.

Feeling: I am feeling the resonance of experience. The dictionary and Encyclopedia Britannica define feelings as showing emotions, passions, sympathies, sensitivities, affections. However, this term is commonly used for a whole range of experiences that are not exactly feelings. For example, "I feel cold" is a sensing of coldness, not a feeling, or "I feel scared of you" is an emotional reaction. The word *feel* had its origins in the Latin *palpo* ("I caress") and the Greek *pselaphao* ("I touch"), and "in psychological terms...*feeling* means to touch inwardly"; it speaks of inner experience.[24] In Psychophonetics, the word *feeling* has a specific meaning: when I feel an inner resonance of an event within my feeling capacity, and I become aware of the feeling that this event stirs up in me, I am inside the experience, feelings well up and radiate from me. Feeling is a more dreamy awareness, less clearly defined, more flowing in its forms, and more fluid and rich in colors, sounds, and personal meaning than in external sense perception and reflection of thinking.[25]

23 Steiner (1981).

24 Zeylmans van Emmichoven (1982:33).

25 Tagar (1994).

Feeling can be regarded as the breathing and healing activity of the soul, as one client describes, "It helps to watch my breathing, to make my breathing come from my belly, to make sure that it's not just being tightly in my chest and I bring it all the way into my belly, up to my head and then I allow it out and I follow it, my consciousness follows that so that I'm actually in tune with that."

Medically, the rhythmic system provides the organic basis for the activity of feeling, where breathing is also connected. At the center of the rhythmic system is the heart, and the heart is the center of the feeling life. We could say that true feeling is breathing, is healing. Breathing into deeper layers of our being allows for the "I am" to be more present, as difficult experiences are often held within us as contractions of held breath, and by breathing into these layers the life forces can move again to release and enhance our true feelings. Yehuda Tagar says: "Feeling is the name for the most inward, intimate and personal response people have to a phenomenon, perceived from inside or from outside."[26] Feeling connects us with our heart and has a central place in our soul life.

Reacting: I am reacting to the experience. Reactions or "re-action" is "action in response to perceived action, action not initiated and governed by the one who acts, but rather triggered by him/her."[27] Reactions consist of desire and the type of reaction relates to the type of desire most active in the soul life. Reactions have the nature of sympathy (attraction) or antipathy (of defense or offence). These desires are ever-changing and moving forms living in our soul life. Some examples of various types of reactions are cravings, cutting off, being aggressive, being numb, intellectualization of emotions, resentment, plus many others.

Psychophonetics sees reactions as "projections of inner content into an outer perception."[28] The nature of a reaction mostly involves automatic, instinctive and repetitive coping behaviors, in which I react to or defend against a perceived threat that reminds me of a

26 Tagar (1994b:5) Persephone College resource material.

27 Tagar (1994b:6).

28 Tagar (1994b:7).

specific event, or I am attracted to it, such as with a craving. That is, in both types of reactions I have been triggered and I am not fully in charge of my response.

> When I see this person coming toward me and I sense he is starting to encroach, I start to close down, to close up; it was awful, I just wanted to go away. I felt a sinking feeling and then I felt all different. It was like I just sunk into this deep hole and just stayed there and from then on everything that person said to me, I just wanted to get up and walk out of that room, I was so triggered...I had no idea why I felt like this.

The fluctuating range of sympathies and antipathies within our inner soul life affect: "our blood circulation, our breathing system and our etheric body."[29] Steiner goes on to give an example of this by saying it is one thing to react to a situation by telling a lie to avoid conflict, but if the consequence is not to make a change, but to feel really satisfied in doing this, then it will have an impact on our circulation, affecting how we breathe and impairing the forces of the etheric life body.

Feelings and reactions can be easily distinguished through gesture or movement in the body. For example, the mixture of reactions and feelings can show in the following ways: a reaction of anger may be covering feelings of sadness or hurt; a feeling of loss may be covered by a reaction of grief; a feeling of conscience may be confused with a reaction of guilt and/or shame; a feeling of compassion may be mixed with a reaction of wanting to rescue. When a moment of a specific experience is gestured, it reveals whether it is a feeling or a reaction response through the way the breath expands or contracts in the gesture. By gesturing and then moving out of this position, we can behold imaginatively the shape of this gesture in front of us, to see and become aware of what is happening in our inner life.

Beholding: I am beholding or observing the experience. Beholding is "being in a position of holding inwardly the expression of the being

29 Steiner (1990:108).

of another person, or [an inner aspect] of myself pictorially."[30] That is, I create a perspective in regard to the impact of an event, and I visualize the emerging images/mental pictures (through imagination) that correspond to the inner dynamics of this perceived, sensed and possibly gestured event.

In *Beholding*, clients describe their experience of beholding after having exited from the position of exploring experientially in gesture a specific event in their life. The process involves bringing attention to the inner dynamics of the specific experience being explored. The clients then gesture this with their body and let it go, stepping away from the position (*exit*) until they are in a position of *beholding* that which was an inner experience and is now externalized imaginatively or pictorially. For example, a client comments:

> I could very much visualize this little person that was like really scared and really broken and really upset and I thought, *Oh my God,* it's also me neglecting that. But I have the power to help this child and to stand back and look at the child in a visual manner helped me want to do that and to see the way that I could. It was just by stepping back and looking at that image in the room, and my response was then to hold, nurture and comfort, it definitely helped me to sit with myself.

Beholding is the activity of the imagination in a conscious meeting between the "I" and a perceived event.

Speaking: I am expressing the experience. Speaking is different from the other aspects as it is regarded as coming from within oneself and going into the outer or inner world as a direct expression of the "I." That is, *I am speaking* and I am being the source of the experience. As such, speaking is "the creative act of the human 'I' expressing itself."[31] This means that I express the event as my own conscious and creative act of expression, communicating to the world. Speaking, in this sense, may not necessarily be verbal. For example, speaking can also be com-

30 Tagar (1994b:9).

31 Tagar (1994b:10).

municated through silence, a gesture, clay, a touch, the way I move and breathe a painting, poetry, or any other medium of human expression. When I am participating in a chosen act, then *I am speaking*.

In the methodology of experience awareness *speaking* is described as having three interrelated activities: *Intending* is our inner mental thinking activity (imagining, intentional dynamics) leading into the act of speaking/expression; *emoting* is our emotional preparation for speaking, which leads our feelings and emotions into speaking/expression; and *urging* is our motivation, will and desire for speaking, which leads our will power and determination into speaking/expression.[32]

Speaking is a complex activity wherein we may not be able to know if someone is really speaking just by observing them. However, through gesturing it becomes clear. I am in the act of speaking when I know that I have digested an experience and am able to express my chosen response to the world and to the experience. For example, in the counseling sessions, each person is encouraged to speak as a basic condition for creating a wish toward action. This is viewed as an active and freely chosen expression of their "I," and speaking in this context is regarded as being permeated by "I am" activity.

We arrive at this *I am* activity following a wish and the action phase of the client's process, often after reactions have been exposed, explored, or exploded. Feelings may then arise such as hurt, joy, sadness, safety, peace, compassion, empathy, tenderness, relaxation, and so on. By coming into a deeper non-reactive connection with our feeling life and aligning feelings with our own values, actions and responsibilities with an outward orientation, then an awareness of this can also be *speaking*. Speaking can be experienced as radiant with presence, situated in the present moment, as an act of creating self and enhancing conditions for being present. Speaking in this sense furthers the embodying of the *I am* with a deeper and fuller breathing in and out, thereby enabling more conscious and intimate relationships with self, others and with the world. Authentic speaking is a major issue for many clients, as one client describes:

32 Tagar (1994b:2).

> The biggest area of change is with confrontation and the reaction of blocked speaking, meaning not able to say what I want to say like "no," or "I don't want to," or "please stop," or any of those things, now I am able to express myself. Before I couldn't even try and speak, I was just scared so now when I am in a difficult situation or fear is stopping me somehow, I stop and think about it and realize that it isn't functional for me and I will breathe and start to feel a relaxation in that breathing and then I can speak calmly.

Based on the threefold body, soul, and spirit, Psychophonetics works in an educative, therapeutic, and creative way. The middle realm of soul bridges between body and spirit, connecting body with spirit. In other words, through our body's senses, we comprehend the world around us; through our soul, we develop impressions of this world, experienced in a whole range of emotions such as desires, aversion, pleasure, giving the world meaning, whereas knowledge of the world is gained through the spirit.[33]

The idea of a threefold nature of soul is not new, as early philosophers such as Plato and Aristotle described soul in this way. More recently, in the field of counseling more integrative approaches emphasize what clients are thinking, feeling and doing. Conscious self-development can be seen as the "I am" awakening to human experience, as well as awakening through the faculties of thinking, feeling and willing.[34] However, thinking, feeling and willing cannot easily be separated, as they are interconnected with each other, with each activity of soul involving the others. In the next chapter, we will explore further how Psychophonetics works with this concept practically and therapeutically.

---

33 In the 1994 edition of his book *Theosophy,* Rudolf Steiner was, in the early 1900s, describing the essential nature of the human being as embracing the three aspects of body, soul and spirit, with other differentiating layers within these.

34 For further reading about thinking, feeling and willing, see Steiner's *The Foundations of Human Experience* (1996) and *A Psychology of Body, Soul and Spirit* (1999).

Chapter 3

The "I AM" Awaking through Thinking, Feeling and Willing

Robin Steele

Counseling offers a safe and caring space for exploring issues and for making changes. As we are born into a relationship from birth and always live in relationship to something or somebody, it is reasonable that when we experience difficulties, we seek a relationship situation in which to explore our issues and any changes we wish to make. This may mean attending counseling and psychotherapy sessions.

Overview and Structure of a Session

Psychophonetics differs from many other approaches in that there is usually a conversation and an action phase in each session. The conversation phase is similar to a person-centered, humanistic type of counseling, but with a transpersonal dimension. The basic form in the conversation phase is to develop a *common picture* (understanding) between the therapist and client of the dynamics in the presenting issue. This means that the counselor invites clients to tell their story, allowing them to experience their own experience and throughout the whole process the counselor encourages clients to say what they truly think, feel and wish to do, even if this disagrees with anything the counselor suggests. In this way, they can establish a rapport and an open, interactive relationship. The counselor may challenge clients if needed, and a crucial aspect in the process is to encourage them to take personal responsibility for their own experience. Once this is done, there is the possibility of making a difference and moving to the next phase of the session. On this basis, the clients are invited to form a *wish*, in their own language, which acts like a guide, purpose, direction or goal for the action phase. The counselor and clients then make an agreement regarding the method of continuing, and the counselor starts plotting for entering the process of the action phase. The clients choose a moment in life relating to the issue central in their wish and recall this experience in the present, restoring it in lived experience with the help of the bodily memory of that experience and stimulated by pictorial memory.

The action phase starts with an exploration through gesturing of the lived experience of the conditions explored verbally during the first phase of the session. From that moment, the nonverbal modes of communication are utilized creatively as ways for exploring, encountering, and/or utilizing whatever is present in each client's lived experience. The integrity of the therapeutic process is held by the *wish*, in which each individual is invited to make a choice about the direction of his/her next step. The wish is an "I am" statement, a choice made toward action in the future. Integration is achieved as experience and reflection weave into self-knowledge throughout the session. Clients can practice the skills learned in the sessions and use them for self-management and self-care between sessions and after therapy is completed.[1]

The statement of a wish determines the next step or threshold in their development. For example, to know myself, to be my authentic self, to release blocked speaking, to express myself on equal terms with another, to know where the anger comes from, to go to the depth of feeling, to have more confidence, to heal my finger, to heal the hurt. Creating the ability to make a wish encourages the client to picture imaginatively. To make a wish is a creative act that implies there is a striving for health and wholeness, as a step toward imagining the possibility of changing and creating something new. As a basis for taking

1 Tagar (1996e).

action, the practitioner needs to create conditions with the client in order to move toward the wish becoming an intentional and decisive act. This means creating a space for meeting and creating conditions for change, wherein each person's wish is respected. The point needs to be made that if a client makes a wish for someone else to change, or for something that is morally or ethically not okay with the practitioner, then this wish would not be accepted in that form. The conversation would continue until the wish was refined to be about the client's own inner change or not. This is also a threshold for the practitioner, to be able to imagine a practical, moral and ethical process for meeting the wish. The process of making a wish is also a threshold for clients to accept responsibility for their own issues and to make a decision to do something about the next step in their development.

Even though the *wish* guides the counselor in how to proceed in the action phase, it is the actual *decision* to take action that becomes the bridge between wishing and action. It is the clients' choice and the counselor may have to help them to recognize and take responsibility for their own choices. As a final step, when clients then *commit* to their decision by taking action, this reinforces the acceptance of their own inner power and resources.

People's *wishes* may indicate that they will be entering an action process of exploration, empowerment and resourcefulness. Or, it may indicate that the focus of the process is on another level, of working with a specific reaction, projection, or threshold experience. Or, their wish may indicate focusing on a specific topic as the starting point.

The following major groups, briefly described, comprise the body of practice of Psychophonetics, using nonverbal modes of knowing:

Conditioning—warming up, conditioning and enlivening the presence of the soul in the body for the exploration process;

Exploration—enhancing clients' ability to explore their internal dynamics between the emotional, biographical, relationship and behavioral dynamics in the present situation;

Empowerment—enhancing clients' ability to speak and respond as they choose in situations and in their interactions with others;

Resourcefulness—invoking a higher dimension of clients' soul and spiritual being through enhancing the faculties of Imagination, Inspiration, and Intuition to the degree that they are ready;

Overcoming reactions—the methodical process of observing the otherwise unconscious automatic responses to threats that limit human development to repetitions of the past;

Owning projections—the methodical process of tracing and observing the shifts in perception and motivation from responding to what is there to what is being triggered by external reality. Owning projections is designed to reclaim the components of the whole of people's potential beings that have been habitually projected onto others in their environment;

Crossing thresholds/levels of estrangement from the "I am"—for example, facing one's shadow or double;

Psychosomatics—for example, headache, pain;

Enlivening/sounds healing—for the nurturing, protection, immune enhancement, restoration, warming and breathing of the life forces;

Special topics—such as decision making, vocational counseling, heart protection, panic attacks, fear of public speaking, stress management, grief and loss, recovery from abuse and addiction, overcoming artistic blocks, team building and others.

Throughout the therapeutic process, the skill of empathy is being developed in counselors through an *inner parallel counseling process*, as a way of re-searching soul processes. This is the skill of deep empathic listening, of developing and deepening the capacity to be aware, to observe and be with the experience of what is happening within the other person's soul life as well as their own. In this process, counselors have to shift their consciousness from self-centered care to the care of others—to be able to differentiate the nature of these activities—allowing for new understanding and clearer perceptions and pictures of an experience, situation or relationship to be present. Engaging with inner processes in a conscious way (in a reflective process of re-searching inner dynamics), allows more creative opportunities for using these experiences in the therapeutic process. For the counselor, deep empathic listening is based on the ongoing conscious development of awakening the faculties of Imagination, Inspiration and Intuition. For me, it is also a practice of developing the heart, as love in action. Then one can take a step beyond empathy. When we meet another with an open mind and heart as well as with an open will, we are in a state of *presence*, or *presencing*,[2] allowing the future to come. This heightened attentiveness to an emerging whole allows for inner shifts of consciousness whereby future possibilities can emerge from our inner knowing and beyond our own self, allowing for the creation of something new.

As the counselor's personal development occurs alongside as an inner parallel counseling process, there is a strong emphasis on the ongoing practical path of the personal, professional and spiritual development of the counselor.

"I AM" Awakening through Thinking, Feeling, and Willing

In the process of therapeutic change, the activity of the "I" makes a difference by being able to penetrate experience and become more present through body and soul. Change comes from this inner force of the "I" in the soul, and when the "I" is not swayed by the forces of thinking, feeling and willing, there is a sense of balance or wholeness experienced. We can see this in situations where we have achieved something new, after first struggling with an old way of being. Psychosophy describes three time streams flowing from past and future and into the present. This means, for example, in the tension between past thoughts holding us back and the wish for a better future, we can enter the center of our beings and become more attentive in the present to our own inner lives. We find our sense of wellbeing and wholeness when we embrace thinking, feeling and willing with more "I am" presence. The challenge is to show this differentiation of soul between thinking, feeling and willing and their expressions in the body, without losing its unity. From this

2 See Scharmer (2007) *Theory U*, in which he describes "presencing" as both presence and sensing, as being in a higher state of attention.

perspective, with the soul dynamics of perception and intuiting, we are participating in three worlds.

Another way of understanding this is to see how these aspects are also connected with our three major bodily systems, involving the head/nerve, metabolic and rhythmic systems. Between the head/nerve–sense system and the metabolic system is the rhythmic system, in which the heart and the lungs are actively involved in breathing and blood circulation. This rhythm of breathing in/out connects us with feeling, in a more dreamlike consciousness,[3] and it is interesting to observe Steiner's view of consciousness as also threefold in the sense of waking, dreaming and sleeping.[4] For example, it is different for an elderly person, like my eighty-seven-year-old mother, when the forces of youth and life are withdrawing, though there is more experience and wisdom present. I find that even though she is less active and needs less sleep, she is more awake in her consciousness.

What are these three activities of soul and how can we come to know them through our *living* experience? They can be summarized briefly as follows: In thinking, I am making sense of the world and giving it meaning, after first perceiving and sensing, and feeling the world within myself. Then, when I become conscious of and can name this experience, I am *thinking*. In my *feeling* soul, all the sensory impressions that activate my inner experience and awareness also stimulate my personal feelings, such as when I feel elated, joyful, loving, lonely or sad. In these activities we act and react in the world through *willing* (doing, action) unconsciously as instinct, drive and desire, or consciously as motivation, wish, intention and decision.[5] Psychophonetics describes three main types of issues: Through *thinking* we can come to know ourselves, to become *oriented*; through *willing* we can encounter, confront situations to become *empowered* and to take action; while through *feeling* we can connect with and invoke the necessary inner/

3 Bott (1984).

4 Steiner (1996).

5 Steiner (1996).

outer *resources* to meet our needs, enabling feelings of connectedness to radiate in our feeling life.[6] The balancing of these three activities can support our true expression:

> To come to one's own genuine, authentic Speaking (and expression). True speaking comes from one's core of being...speaking that is not reactive, nor avoiding or compensating or coming to please. True speaking is the breathing of one's soul [and]...that expression is the Speaking of the "I am."[7]

In this way, our intention, feelings and the urge to speak are embraced inwardly in a harmonious way by the "I" in the act of speaking and expressing. These three activities overlap and interweave. For example, we can go through phases of coming to know something about ourselves to gain perspective on the dynamics of our inner/outer life; or we can have issues with power, or anger, of being blocked and of something to release, to free ourselves from some hindrance, to overcome fear, to gain courage; or we can nurture, access inner and/or outer resources, make spiritual connections, and meet inner needs. All these aspects are ways of becoming more conscious, of coming into our own true speaking and expressing in our own unique ways.

How do we awaken to the differentiated activities in our soul life and how, in the therapeutic context of Psychophonetics, does the "I" awaken through thinking, feeling and willing? In addressing this question, these activities will be described as main themes, as experiential structures of soul experience, using examples. Only some, not all, of the main basic processes will be described, as details of all of these processes would

6 The theoretical foundation for this interpretation has come from the work of Yehuda Tagar who further developed *thinking, willing and feeling* in the early 1990s as three types of counseling issues: exploration/orientation, encounter/empowerment and resourcefulness. A description of the three types of issues was first published in 1994, in a paper given by Tagar called, "Awakening to the Resounding of Human Experience" at the Transpersonal Studies National Conference, Australian Consciousness and Action, in Perth, WA.

7 Tagar (1994:31).

contain a book in itself and the following chapters contain many practical examples of these processes as well. These activities are presented as thinking (exploration–orientation), willing (encounter–empowerment) and feeling (resourcefulness nurturing/providing/invoking), as a process of discovery, insight, and meaning-making. It needs to be remembered that differentiating these soul activities does not mean they are separate and isolated categories; each one is interrelated and interweaving with the others. For example, clients may enter a process whereby they need to connect with their inner resources before encountering something fearful or may just need time to digest some aspect before continuing in another session, to become oriented in relation to their issue.

All the processes in Psychophonetics are viewed as guiding principles for exploring experience phenomenologically through the body using the nonverbal tools as modes of knowing. They are not set or prescribed procedures.

This chapter is an introduction to three basic groups of processes: orientation, empowerment and resourcefulness. Further descriptions of the other groups in this body of practice will come in future books. However, some other processes are described in the following chapters, for example, Darcy's "threshold" experience in *Darcy's Journey out of Depression*, plus the chapters on topics such as grief and loss, healing past childhood sexual abuse and working with addiction.

Processes of Exploration Leading to Orientation—in Thinking

Orientation means being able to create a perspective within our own field of experience, to find out or know something, to have a realization, to gain an insight, to see the picture.[8] However, denial and self-doubt can be a major hindrance to self-awareness and truth, but can also allow the client to sense and gesture experience and then to observe and reflect on this, bringing greater clarity and perspective in thinking, as a client describes:

---

8 Seeing the picture means thinking, as pictorial imaginative thinking, thinking in images, as picturing.

> It was amazing to find out and to have a greater clarity and understanding about past hurts and triggers...I mean first I had to gesture the situation, feel it, find a sound and then at the end was the clay. I looked at the clay that was there and to accumulate all this in front of me and bring it together in one clay model, was quite difficult...I had been very fearful of revisiting and when I revisited it, I felt great 'cause I actually did it myself. It was a really wonderful feeling to go through the gesturing and to do it myself through the clay...the clarity of seeing it in clay was quite profound for me...there was a different perspective completely.

When something is not known it is usually behind our conscious awareness. When we face an issue of concern it then is in front of our consciousness and we can see what is going on. Yehuda Tagar describes becoming oriented as liberating:

> Whenever I stop in my tracks...and turn around to look at myself, at my direct experience of the present moment, taking an interest in my experience as it is...I have started to move, to liberate myself from being locked in unconscious identification with a part of me, into the healing dynamics of the whole of me; I have made a shift from being a passive receiver of the effect of my life, into being the active co-creator of its meaning for me. And then real healing can start.[9]

Becoming oriented in thinking can be not only liberating but, as another client found, focusing within through sensory awareness to explore inner dynamics can become very revealing:

> With the drawings and gestures they revealed to me visually something that in the past I could maybe only have been able to guess and think around and hypothesize about. But these were concrete. When you know something is true there's something in the body that breathes, there's something in the body that goes "aha."

The first step is coming to know the details of an inner dynamic, through exploration, observation and understanding:

9 Tagar (1996a:24).

> First of all, recognizing, second, understanding and third of all loving that particular behavior for what use it was for me when I was a child, and seeing that it wasn't useful now as an adult...It allowed me to look at everything to do with that and healing it with that patience and love, knowing that I had to use these behaviors because I wasn't fed or I was abused or in some way trying to protect myself and now knowing I don't have to do that.

Enter–Exit–Behold

Objectifying ourselves through enter–exit–behold is the core process of the action exploration. In the context of a session and in conjunction with the wish, this means *entering* bodily into an experience and then *exiting*, to see (*behold*) what is happening. There are two ways to *enter* an experience: from sensing or from beholding. The focus could be what is happening right now in the body, or it could be to recall a moment that exemplifies the pattern being focused on, allowing the body memory to resonate and either bring it into a bodily sensation or focus on the memory picture of it in the mind. By *entering* this moment and expressing it through moving and gesturing with the whole body, the inner character/s that flow through our soul life can be brought into visible form. After being *in* the experience, the gesture is shaken off as we *exit* (by moving *out* of this position physically) and observe the dynamics of the gesture in the empty space left behind. When a gesture is formed with our whole body, then let go and exited, a picture emerges in our visual memory, as if an imprint was left behind in space, created by the gesture. This pattern or character can then be observed or beheld imaginatively by an objective observer. Once observed, this pattern can be explored from any point of view, aspect and angle. By externalizing or ex-forming the internal dynamic energetically, it gives some distance by separating the issue from our personal identity, freeing the client to enact and express the inner drama in which there can be many characters and roles. The client can also *enter in* again through visualization, sensation, gesture and sound into every aspect of an inner pattern, bringing up other aspects to consciousness. Once the client feels oriented with a clear perspective on the dynamic, the next step can be identified. One client describes her experience of becoming oriented:

> It brought memory back into particular situations where I had been yelled at or belted and I couldn't, as a child, be able to say what I wanted to say. The change was that I got to be able to see, everything was in front of me so I was able to tangibly, visually see who I was...That means I have a clearer picture of who I am...there is full awareness of all the aspects of me that all have the potential to make a whole of me, without me not knowing what is going on in my body and in my psyche, in my head and my mind. I'm actually able to say, "Okay, this is how I react when I'm in this situation," or, "This is how I project if I am in this situation."

"The orientation grows as the exploration deepens, through the perspective created in this process."[10] The next step could include anything from further exploration, to nurturing, confrontation or overcoming a reaction and most likely would include using the sounds of human speech to sound-name various aspects in the process. All the processes are uniquely designed to meet the particular client's situation. Participating in an enter–exit–behold process is not always an easy experience and there can be an initial resistance, fear or self-doubt that has to be overcome creatively. Our defense mechanisms may become stronger if fear is triggered and there may be resistance. This may include times when it becomes difficult for clients to *exit* their experience fully.

Bamboo

The *bamboo* process is basically an extension of an *exit* in the *enter–exit–behold* process. When clients exit from an experience but are not able to create a clear perspective between their consciousness and their inner content, then they are regarded as still being *in* their content. In addition, clients who appear to be *out* and have some perspective, on a cognitive level, may actually still be *in* on an emotional and body-response level. In the *bamboo* process, when clients are still *in* the expe-

10 Tagar (1994:30).

rience, the counselor brings their focus to how they are in the body right now; to express and embody this in gesture; then to exit this gesture. If clients are *out* they will be able to *behold* the previous position as well as the original position. Some distance is a precondition for cognitive awareness. If clients are still not out, then the process of exiting from this position is repeated for as many times as needed until they can *behold* the previous gesture of the particular experience, are more present and their breathing is more relaxed. The *bamboo* process is an essential element for the safety of the action phase and also can enable further deepening of clients' processes. As teamwork is a basic ethic of this approach, the clients have to be able to return to being in the observer position to give meaning to their experiences and to make the choices in their processes.

Russian Doll

Whereas *bamboo* is a process of exiting, the *Russian doll* process extends the *enter* of *enter–exit–behold*. This process is relevant when further entering is needed through sensing and gesturing or through drawings, until the core, deeper layers or inner chamber of the dynamic is reached. The process includes a basic *enter–exit–behold,* and in the *beholding* position there is a sense or feeling that there is more to know, of deeper layers to explore. The clients enter into and become the experience again for as many times as needed, until the imaginative picture of the inner forces are revealed and known. After each *enter*, the clients *exit* from the previous position to *behold* and visualize from this new beholding position, and engage in a process of *staging* or describing what is being experienced before deciding to *enter* a deeper layer of the same experience.

An example of this process: After *entering–exiting–beholding*, a young man senses there is more in there: "I can feel it in the body; it's deeper in." The counselor inquires, "Where deeper in?" The man replies "in the chest." He enters into the chest and curls up into a tight gesture, then exits again. He beholds this and says, "I sense my heart is aching," so he enters into the aching heart and finds a feeling of loneliness held deep within. Upon exiting, he remembers an incident from his childhood, and the feelings that had been held in for many years could now be felt, expressed and integrated.

The Russian doll process is a conscious activity wherein the client chooses to *enter, enter, enter,* with no difficulty in *beholding.*

The Experience of "Leaving the Body"

The body can become an instrument of awareness and meaning, but we may experience avoiding feelings of pain by our consciousness *leaving the body, excarnating* or *dissociating.* In the literature on dissociation, the process is seen primarily as experiences that are not integrated into the whole but are stored in the memory as separate fragments of sensory perceptions or affective states that can keep happening in daily life when there is too much stress, anxiety or confronting situations. Dissociation can also involve de-realization and depersonalization when a person is traumatized or "spacing out."[11] Other therapists refer to dissociation as implying a splitting of awareness in various forms. Some examples of this are cutting off feelings, feeling disembodied, amnesia and fainting, and the extreme forms are when the whole personality becomes separated from consciousness.

In Psychophonetics, *excarnating* means our consciousness has left the body. For instance, a client who came to counseling to address her experience of past abuse describes her way of coping in difficult situations:

> I can turn off pain if I want to, at the blink of an eye and it's not there...I can notice what's in the body but I cannot feel, when I come back to the body I can feel. I learned to leave my body when it was being beaten, so that I didn't feel the pain, and I'm very good at leaving my body.

From clinical practice and research it has been found that young children learn to leave their bodies when they feel threatened in expe-

11 Kirkengen (2001:114).

riences such as sexual abuse or from any traumatic experience, with the consequence that they are still not fully present in the body as an adult.[12] This retreat from self affects the flow of life forces and the sense of wellbeing. New ways need to be found to be more present in the body.

The experience of *leaving the body* is accepted as that person's reality. When people are asked where they are, they usually perceive themselves as being away from where the physical body is. When clients are invited by the counselor to move physically to be in this disembodied position, they can usually describe very clearly what they see from this point of view, regarding the experience of the body that is left in the previous position. From this position of being out of the body, the experience of what happened to them can be seen but not felt, and from there, a different choice can be made to start the process of returning consciously home to the body. The importance of listening and being present to the sensations in the body can help us be more in the present moment and not be stuck in past habits.

What is this experience of *leaving the body* like? How do we know if we are doing this? One client describes this experience as a feeling of emptiness in the head, where she can be talking but does not feel present: "It just seems to be on some sort of automatic pilot... and I am slipping off out of consciousness." Sound work is a very effective way of creating an energetic shift and change in the body: "Each time I make a sound and gesture I give myself more space and I was able to break down the vibrations of the negative energy with a counteracting sound and it feels like I have involved the whole of me, to heal the whole of me, and not just the mind."

The process of working with the client's experience of *leaving the body* is also described in some of the following chapters, especially in the chapter on healing past childhood sexual abuse.

In becoming more oriented, it is important that we become aware of when "I am" is consciously present or not present, when "I am" *in* or

12 Tagar (2003).

out of my body, in order to really know what is happening in our inner life and in the world around us. It is also important for the counselor to remain consciously present. Retreating from the self can happen at any point whenever fear is triggered, and the task is to become aware of how these fears and habitual coping actions are triggered and to learn other more constructive ways of meeting these situations. Staying present means being able to remain consciously present in a situation. One client describes how she experiences *coming into presence*:

> If I'm listening to a person and they trigger something, and I feel that sinking feeling of going into myself I say, "No no no, there's no need for that, I'm safe, it's okay," and it's like a bubble coming up to the surface of still water and just going "plop," and its presence is there and I'm here, and it feels like I've suddenly woken up and I'm ready to listen to what that person's saying crisply, clearly and without any connotations of negativity toward myself. So I feel like I've woken, all of a sudden again. Yeah, it's like a bubble coming to the surface and going "plop, here I am, I'm alive, and I'm clear."

The Experience of Resistance

Resistance is one of the major reasons that people don't or won't change, especially in engaging with an action method, as it may mean there are feelings of being more vulnerable and exposed. On this basis, the client's motivation and feelings of safety in the counseling space are crucial elements in overcoming resistance. The counselor can do this by warming up the room, by being compassionate, empathic, present, nonjudgmental, accepting and patient with the client, or by making a safety contract with the client if needed.

> Resistance...That in her which is so scared of the feelings which might be there desperately trying to escape from facing something inescapable in the deep. Once brought into gesture, she could let go, move out of that position and look back into the vacant space she left behind, where that remarkable gesture still echoed for both of us in its intense reality. She could "see" that fear for what

> it was. It had nothing to do with the holiday, the partner, the plans, the practicalities of life's struggles that were blamed before for her confusion. In the empty space where she has just been, she now beheld the little frightened girl having no tangible support which she once was, who, for some reason was triggered in that holiday, was again triggered as threatening and surfacing into her feeling life and flooding the consciousness of the mature woman with her fears. Once made conscious, embraced with awareness, this little girl can be taken care of by her owner.[13]

By accepting and becoming interested in resistance and working with this experience phenomenologically, it can be included in the process as something to come to know in itself, rather than something to overcome or fight against. On the path of self-knowledge, as clients become aware of how their activity of thinking is actually working, they can discover how they may speculate, justify or deny experience.

Compassion—Choosing Attitude

Facing the unknown may not be easy, especially in situations in which we become confused, when there are conflicting inner voices keeping us feeling disoriented. How do we become clearer about this? One example of this is when a client was learning to care for and heal her heart, she described feeling confused and wounded, as well as not liking that feeling and trying to deny its presence, while at the same time knowing that she needed to take care of and heal her heart. With the diversity of these internal voices the client's wish was, "to gain a clearer perspective, to become self-accepting and compassionate." Three internal voices or perspectives appeared in this experience and can be named as: the one in need or wounded one, the self-hater or judging one, and the compassionate one.

In this situation, the Psychophonetics process is called the *Compassion Triangle.*[14] By entering a process of *enter–exit–behold*

---

13 Tagar (1996a:21).

14 Tagar (1995c).

and *staging*[15] this client moves from one position to another, exploring the three positions from the inside and from the outside until, through the activity of *beholding,* she gains perspective regarding all three positions. By externalizing the inner dynamics, she is able to distinguish between her feelings of vulnerability that need to be cared for, her reaction that was judging and denying the need, and her compassionate self who could observe both the need and the judgment. When being compassionate, the client is able to see the full picture and become oriented in regard to her internal dynamic. From this position she can choose her next step. In this case, she decides to invoke an inner source of love and compassion, which she provides to herself in gesture, visualization and with the sound "*mmm.*" Through this process she created conditions for feeling a sense of heart safety. We usually feel compassion toward others, but we can also feel and direct compassion toward ourselves for our own self-care, nurturing and healing, as an act of intimacy and empathy.

In summary, the exploration of an issue through the process of body awareness and expression can lead to an orientation in our thinking. This means being able to perceive the activity of our own emotional and feeling life; to perceive our own responses to this activity of the inner soul life; to perceive the effects of these inner patterns on our thinking, feeling and willing and on our wellbeing; as well as becoming clearer in our perceptions of others. Becoming oriented in thinking may be all that is needed, or perhaps being oriented leaves the following questions: What is the next step in my journey of self-development? Is knowing enough, do I have to overcome some hindrance, is there something missing, or do I need more of something?

---

15 *Staging* is a term used in Psychophonetics for deepening *beholding*, by looking into the different layers of the specific experience being beheld, to clarify imaginatively, to decide and create conditions for the next step, or as a way of integrating the revealed inner content. Tagar (1993a).

Processes of Encounter Leading to Becoming Empowered—Taking Action

The process of encounter leading to becoming more empowered means developing the capacity to confront, within our own inner experience, any pattern of limitation, fear and traces of invasions or pressures that may compromise our potential or expression, and to reclaim our personal power and assert our presence within our own inner space in order to speak with our authentic voice. Empowerment means coming into one's own authority.

It is not unusual to find ourselves and others struggling with being defensive in interactions with others, or being affected by negative influences, and experiencing a range of emotions such as feeling disempowered, defeated, oppressed, weakened, overpowered, compromised, abused, violated, stressed by critical internal voices, unable to confront others or to speak clearly and assertively. These are all issues of power. In the therapeutic context, the assumption that Psychophonetics makes is that this tendency is embedded within us as a repetitive habit or reaction that reoccurs or is projected into new situations.

Through the exploration and orientation process, an issue of power may emerge as the source of this pattern. Before we can create a change in this pattern, we have to own the energetic inner force of the exposed dynamic as our own inner dynamic, that is, we cease to blame external sources of power. In order to change the inner dynamic and to create a more conscious "I am" way of being, resources need to be available and accessed, in readiness to confront, reclaim, recycle and transform the inner dynamic into an outer capacity. One client describes this as, "setting up boundaries to stop people getting into my space and triggering different things within me...as I was giving away my power. Through the sessions I've been just able to stand up to that and say what I wanted to say, or say how I felt, or just say no."

Unblocking

The basic Psychophonetics process for overcoming any limiting or destructive reactionary behavioral pattern is called *reversing,* of which *unblocking* is a major example.[16] Through an action exploration process of *enter–exit–behold,* leading to an *unblocking* process, Yehuda Tagar describes the following elements that have to become visible:

> A clear picture of the internal dynamic resulting in the disempowerment experience; [Identifying and distinguishing the offensive from the defensive components of the experience]; the character, gesture, shape and sound of the invading/pressuring power; and the internal posture of the receiving end of that invasion, one's own vulnerable part.[17]

Guided by the above activity, the act of *unblocking* can be done by the client entering into the experience of suffering, for a moment, then replaying the dynamics of the invasion in sound and gesture, usually replayed by the counsellor sounding the client's sound, which can lead to stirring an internal natural reaction against it. This organic response is expressed and practiced in gesture, movements, and sounds and the new inner strength is tested and practiced until the person remains present without reacting, in a clear personal inner soul space, as a preparation and a new basis for meeting everyday life situations. To complete the process, there are a variety of creative ways that can be used to maintain and to grow this personal space and to consolidate a sense of a personal boundary, through being connected with one's inner and outer resources.[18]

---

16 The process of *unblocking*—for example, of an emotional knot in the stomach—was first described by Tagar in 1991 in the article "Philophonetics: Language for the Whole Being." This article includes a series of photos that gives a visual picture of the guiding principles in this process.

17 Tagar (1999:260).

18 Further detailed descriptions of an empowerment process can be found in case-study format: Sherwood, P., and Tagar, Y. (2000a); Steele (2008) and Tagar (1996e).

Living with and Overcoming Fear

Fear can often be present as a major obstacle, stopping us from confronting aspects of our inner life and from speaking our truth. We may need to develop certain soul capacities. For instance, one man had to develop an *inner strength* to find the *courage* to overcome his fear of speaking about what he thought and felt. Another client commented, "Before, in confrontation, I was very frightened, I wanted to hide, I avoided people that I thought would be like that [threatening]" and where she felt: "I cannot breathe, I need to hide, I need to run, you know." By accessing courage, she faced the fear and was able to say, "I can breathe, I can say what I need to say, I can stand strong." The counseling process involves not just clients having a wish or intention, but also activating their will and courage to take action as well as gathering the needed resources.

The task is not to get rid of fear, but to make it an opportunity to develop capacities of inner strength. Rather than avoiding fearful situations and becoming isolated from the world, we can learn to face the fear within as a starting point for facing fear in the world.[19] The two primal reactions of fear and anger arise initially from the survival instinct as a warning to keep us alive. Fear may also have the tendency to create anger, and once the fear is faced, there may be a release of anger initially in the urge to speak that which hadn't or couldn't be spoken in the past, which also clears the way for taking care of any hurt feelings. A client describes her process:

> The anger was putting on a lid, I felt like I was suppressed, I didn't have any air, I was in this chamber and I couldn't breathe. I just went into that, and so that was I was not allowed to express myself as a child. I went into the inner child experience with all those feelings about not being able to express my anger and then I sit with her and say there's me here as an adult and...I can cuddle myself and I said to myself, it's going to be okay, I will look after you, and keep you safe. I'm learning to express myself in a way I want to. So it was very powerful.

19 Sardello (1999).

One of the reasons people choose to go to counseling is because it offers a safe space where they can face doubts, fears or self-hatred, not alone, but with the counselor as a supportive presence. Doing this provides an opportunity for learning new ways of creating a safe *inner space,* by becoming more self-aware, empowered and nurtured, learning how to live and express ourselves differently in the world.

Releasing Blocked Speaking

Fear can block our speaking and is a common issue in counseling. Blocked speaking means: Not being able to say what you want to say or to express yourself. The ability to speak how we really feel or think is held back, and fear of public speaking is one of the most commonly experienced fears. The following example gives a sense of how this fear may be experienced:

> If the request, for instance, was to overcome the paralyzing fear of public speaking, and during the Action–Exploration phase one discovers that in occasions of speaking in front of people a black cloud is descending upon one's chest, preventing it from being able to breathe—then that black cloud has to be confronted, dissolved, digested or "recycled."[20]

Blocked speaking may also manifest in someone who is a good listener but rarely speaks up, or in people who are pleasers and don't like fighting, or in those people who keep secrets, for whatever reason. One way of working creatively through an issue of *blocked speaking* is with clay, which gives a firsthand experience of the shapes, sounds and inner meanings of the experience. Taking an active interest in our experience and in the present moment becomes an experience of soul, of being in our center. When we are able to make conscious choices and not just be caught in reacting to situations, becoming more of our true and non-reactive selves, this *is* a transformation.

20 Tagar (1994:30). This paper gives a more detailed description of the process.

Artistic expression through such mediums as clay, painting and drawing are powerful ways of entering into a phenomenon of knowing intuitively, moving beyond sensory experience. In my experience and understanding from working with artistic expression over a long time, when my imagination is encouraged and I bring this into something created with my own hands, then deeper connections and knowing can be made visible. Creating through clay or drawing *makes* me and *through it I become*, means that releasing one's expression and speaking is a powerful "I am" gesture. Some people, however, may sense vulnerability in doing this and may need the consolidation of a sense of a personal inner space with the creation of an inner energetic boundary.

Re-creating an Inner Soul Space

Personal space can be described as an energetic dynamic and the following description gives a sense of this:

> These are real bodily dynamics on the subtle, energetic level, invisible to the eye and only visible through their externally expressed symptoms. The boundary of personal space is a sort of a second skin which energetically protects us from the invasion of other people's energies as our first skin protects us from the elements of the physical surrounding.[21]

In the experience of creating a clearer inner soul space for the "I am" presence, personal inner boundaries may be needed. Personal space can exist on four overlapping layers: the physical—in our physical surroundings, my "home" is a space in which I can relax, work and live how I want to; in our life energy, breathing and warming, I can expand my energy and warmth space around me; the astral/soul—in my feelings, emotions and power relations, I can feel on an equal standing with another person or I may feel disempowered in the presence of a particular person; and spiritually—in my inner sense of "I" and sense of freedom, I can feel at "home" spiritually, with an open

21 Tagar (1999:261).

heart and with an inner strength. The example of a sense of *home* can overlap in all these areas.

We have within us a prototype or an inner knowing of how our personal space can be, as an ideal, as a sense of wholeness, or as a sense of wellbeing. We have this knowing, as we know when we feel our space has been compromised, breached or intruded upon in its various layers.

A *Guarding* gesture is a useful ritual for maintaining "I am" presence and an inner soul space. This ritual involves two faculties and performs two complementary functions: Holding a vulnerable inner part with one hand, in a protective gesture, while guarding against a perceived external threat to this vulnerability, with the other arm stretched outward, in a guarding gesture. This is usually done initially in the context of a counseling session, using movement, sound and visualization. It can then be practiced anytime as a way of protecting and guarding a personal soul space, enabling more resilience when faced with a confronting situation in everyday life.[22]

By becoming more aware of how our soul space can become compromised, we can strive to reclaim and maintain this by creating healthy inner boundaries. For instance, past experiences may restrict possibilities in the present, thereby compromising how we want to live. We may become compromised from the inside by what we do to ourselves, by negative self-talk, fears and doubts. Or, we may feel compromised from our interactions with others and by how well we are able to maintain our sense of self in the presence of the other. This is evident when we react and project onto others, thereby losing our sense of "I" through these habitual patterns of behavior with other people. Some examples are: meeting another's need at all costs, pleasing others, seeking approval from others, avoiding conflict, making oneself smaller, or not expressing one's own feelings.

Personal space can also be compromised through an external event or circumstance that relates to our basic needs for food, shelter and physical safety, but from the therapeutic perspective, by expanding our

22 Tagar (1999).

space of consciousness we can hopefully better deal with these challenges. We could ask, once created, what type of space does it then become? Is creating this space an ongoing process of becoming? How do "I" inhabit this space? How do "I" relate with others and how do we create spaces between us? And how do we allow the "Other" (the universal) to be present in this space? How does our inner space open up to the world? I leave these questions as a source of further contemplation, meditation, imagination, dreaming and action. I leave this space open.

Distinguishing between Guilt and Conscience

Another common aspect that can arise in our lives relates to guilt and conscience. The feeling of conscience can often be confused with guilt and/or shame, and become mixed, as the language can be the same for both. One client found that she experienced a major shift by working through a reaction of guilt in one of her counseling sessions to distinguish it from her conscience, and through this she became clearer in her own authority and speaking. Through gesturing and finding how this dynamic lives and is reflected in the soul, we can then distinguish guilt from conscience. For example, from my experiential work with clients, I have observed that usually in experiences of guilt, there may be a sense of cringing, tightness, and hardness in the gestures, with an inner accusing voice toward oneself; while in positions of conscience, there may be a sense of being more true and upright, with more "I am" presence. Shame may also be present, with the client being more in a mode of hiding, blushing. Shame is more inner and soft in nature. Coming to know and accept the moral basis for what compounds the destructive nature of guilt can be liberating and allows people to experience how they really feel. Once an issue of conscience is clarified, there is usually a release of feeling energy with a sense of relief and freedom.

Guilt and reluctance to express true feelings can be a hindrance in the healing process of the heart and of one's whole being. We have only one heart, and to open our heart to others and to close it to our self is damaging, to the heart and to our whole being. As we gain more inner certainty of conscience, we also develop the necessary strength to overcome further obstacles and accept the consequences of our actions. Guilt is a reaction, and when not resolved it can bring out the worst in us, whereas conscience is a feeling for the truth and potentially can bring out the best in us.

Disappearing

Becoming more empowered is not just being able to confront situations, but can also be an action of finding a safe inner space, inside the body, when faced with a threat. We often do this unconsciously, until we learn to stay present in a confronting situation, or until we have done something to change the inner dynamics that can disempower us. A client describes this activity: "I felt a sinking feeling and then I felt all different. It was like I just sunk into this deep hole and just stayed there . . . all I did was sink inside and hide. . . . Oh my God, I disappeared."

If we are not ready to confront an outer situation or an inner dynamic, then maybe the safest action is to hide or disappear, to protect ourselves and to have some time in order to connect with the needed inner resources, to be potentially present in the confronting situation at another time. The drama of this process is like hiding in a safe cubby house, being there and enhancing that space until we have been there long enough and are ready to come out and be present in the world again. The process is to learn to stay more present and in connection with our inner resources while in a confronting situation, or, if we choose to retreat, then this can be an appropriate conscious action.

Soul empowerment enables us to awaken to old defense mechanisms which have compromised our spirit, to enable us to digest and to take charge of our emotional life, to clear an inner space, so the "I am" can arrive and find a home in body and soul with a stronger sense of inner authority.

The Healing Power of Sound

We use sounds to match and to resonate exactly with the vibration of particular inner dynamics of experience, such as in the process of *unblocking* and *creating an inner space and boundary*, as well as a way of meeting inner needs and for healing. Sounds are a powerful resonating and therapeutic tool and sound therapy is an integral part of the therapeutic process. A woman describes what it means for her:

> Old patterns of behavior can be removed by sound and gesture. I was able to break down the vibrations of these things with a counteracting sound and it seems like I've involved the whole of me to heal the whole of me, and not just the mind. So the whole of me heals because of that. As the counselor is working with me, as she brings to me the sound of the force which I have found, I actually have a bodily reaction, a reaction within the body. I first find the sound and they use that sound and then I find a counter sound to break the vibrations of that sound down.

Resourcefulness, or accessing resources, is usually part of each therapeutic issue, and we nearly always include some element of resourcefulness and sound work to complete a therapeutic process. Whether it is an orientation, empowerment or resourcefulness type of issue, they are all interrelated and need to be integrated.

Processes of Resourcefulness Leading to Nurturing, Providing for Inner Needs, or Invoking Inner Resources (in Feeling)

How do we embrace our thinking and willing with feeling? We can connect to inner resources using sounds, as the resonance dynamics of the sounds live in the life body and can resound with the quality that is needed at that time. These qualities can be expressed through the breath, in sensing, imagining, visualizing, moving and sounding. Resourcefulness in this context means connecting with and enhancing the inner qualities of feelings through nurturing and providing self-care, or through the invocation of an inner source of strength or of some other feeling quality that is needed. Accessing resources may be relevant as part of completing an orientation and/or empowerment process, but some of these processes themselves can also be relevant for becoming more resourceful. For example, hiding or disappearing from facing a fearful encounter may be the only way of finding time-out and a safe place in which to connect to inner resources; while the process of moving from an unconscious reaction to speaking openly is also a way of re-creating connections with inner resources that enable authentic speaking.

In the therapeutic context, resourcefulness can be described as taking care of our own needs, manifesting and connecting with some quality we need, such as joy, peace or calmness; of accessing an inner source, such as a presence, nature spirits, or a knowing; caring for our inner being, nurturing (for example, of an inner child) and protecting self (such as by creating an imaginary dome around oneself), with self-care gestures and sounds of the body and soul that is in need. Resourcefulness connects us in our feeling and soul life as feelings of presence and beingness with our sensitivity, compassion, and our love.

Initially, however, clients may come to counseling because they feel a sense of disconnection from their inner resources, and through the therapeutic process they can be in a safe place to confront the depth of their need and the missing of it. Invoking is another aspect of resourcefulness. Invoking is done through visualization, gesture and sounds, to activate the imagination and to create an invocation of a quality that is felt to be missing in the soul.

The Experience of Breathing

How we are breathing is an essential aspect of wellbeing and good health on all levels of our being. In my doctoral research study, participants were asked to describe the difference that the changes experienced through Psychophonetics counseling had made in their life. One participant said the essence was in the *breathing*:[23]

> *"Haahh"... If that breath could just be said what that change is, that is what the change is. Now I feel much more relaxed, much more*

23 Steele (2005:183).

confident, I like me more and I trust myself more and befriend myself more and I feel more whole, Mmmm, there's absolutely an enormous difference. "Haahh"... it has been joy to me because I feel strength in myself that I am who I am. It's a feeling of peace within myself, I feel very relaxed and even the way I walk is different, more free, not so tight and I accept myself the way I am now, too. It is a relief that I do not have to be acting to make people like me.

In the past, this person had lived in a lot of fear and anxiety, which meant that her breathing was contracted, affecting her ability to observe clearly and to take in new experiences, with a consequence that when she didn't breathe properly her ability to express feelings was affected. Breathing is a basic process of life and while fear can hinder our breathing and growth, breathing with ease and being creative can deepen our relationship with life. For instance, our capacity for breathing, warming and taking care can become a soul quality of intense, warm interest in the world, while the life processes of secretion, maintenance, growth and reproduction can give the body a feeling of depth, energy and vitality. A client highlights the importance of breathing in her process: "When you know something is true there's something in the body that breathes, there's something in the body that goes 'Aha.'"

Providing and Nurturing

Providing for and nurturing inner needs are common activities in learning to become more resourceful. Each person's capacity to imagine is encouraged, and the sounds are used as a powerful way of healing and of meeting inner needs. For example, one client went through a profound experience of grief and loss of her husband, in which she experienced feelings of emptiness in the core of her being and being in a void, to finding joy and heart warmth and the spiritual resources to create a new life for herself: "Until the heart had actually been healed and been given these nurturing sounds and the love it required I couldn't experience joy. The sounds made a big change for me." When our whole being is involved in a process, there is a resounding in the soul that is always available.

In personal transformative work, when we look only outside for our needs to be met and ignore the possibility of making a direct connection with our inner world, we may become more dependent upon others to give us what we need. This is where codependency in relationships and addictive behaviors can potentially develop. When we look inward to experience a missing quality, to see what is happening, then we have the opportunity to reconnect with an inner need. In doing this, however, we may experience an inner block that stops us from connecting with a needed quality. This inner emotional block will need to be faced and cleared if the health of our breathing is going to be restored. In awakening the "I am" into becoming more conscious, we can honor our whole self, rather than having disowned aspects of our self gaining power within our psyche.

In owning our inner patterns, we are awakening to experience and changing by developing a sensitivity and communication with our inner needs by developing ways of meeting those needs. Finding resources means also being able to find those outer resources that resonate within to enrich our feeling life, like being in the garden or going for a walk along the beach, or connecting with nature as a resource. If needed, we can also recall the echo of these experiences in our imagination, to reconnect with feeling these qualities again if a garden is not available. For example, a client says, "I feel connected to the plants and I feel connected, whole and energetic, it gives me energy, it nurtures the etheric, makes me feel more alive and energetic."

There is a wide variety of resources that are supportive for taking action such as a connection with nature or a connection with spiritual help. We do not always have to *do* something to be connected with our feelings. *Being* aware and present in our feelings can keep us in touch with our soul life and our lived experience. Just *being in* how we are feeling and bringing more beauty into our lives is important.[24] We can find ways in our daily life to be more present in a soulful way so that we can begin to live in and with beauty.

24 Tagar (1995b).

Self-parenting

A common aspect of resourcing experienced by many people is the act of *self-parenting.* This means the adult is parenting an *inner child* in need of attention and care. The dynamics of an *inner child* can determine our behavior, responses, how well we connect with or are cut off from our inner resources, energy, relationships, wellbeing, creativity, purpose and depth of meaning in our life. The ability to self-parent, or to take care of our inner needs, has implications in the world for how we are as parents of our own children, in being able to meet their needs, as the following example shows.

A mother comes for a session because she is concerned about the loss of friendship with her teenage daughter, as they had been close, but are now fighting a lot. She has become angry and controlling toward her daughter who is not taking any notice and rejects her. When we talk about this and what life was like for her as a teenager, the mother recalls conflicts with her parents when she was a teenager, and how they tried to impose their values and restrictions on her. In this conversation she realizes that her daughter's behavior is similar and she doesn't want to have this repeated any more. Through an action process, she comes to understand the inner dynamics and learns to "parent" her inner teenager with more compassion and care, as a process of self-parenting. In the following session, she describes how a positive change has happened in her relationship with her daughter, as she is able to communicate with her without trying to judge or control her.

The hope and resilience we need for ourselves as adults involves taking care by listening to what is happening within the body, in our inner life, and accepting these experiences as a source of truth for ourselves. Perhaps we all have an opportunity to contribute to humanity by creating new forms of relationships in which we not only listen but also hear through our feeling heart what is happening, not just within ourselves and with our own children, but for future generations. The ability to self-parent invokes higher aspects of one's self and can restore an open and direct communication between our consciousness and our higher being, allowing for the possibility of creating a different relationship with self and others. The chapter "The Inner Dimensions of Parenting and Self-parenting" expands upon this issue in more detail.

These processes, or guiding principles, are meant to encourage our imaginative, intuitive and creative capacities for exploring our inner and outer life, leading us to be more in our "I am" presence, with more true speaking, more intimate relationships and in deeper communion with self, others and the world, to live and further our deeds of destiny.

Thinking, Feeling and Willing Leading into Speaking

Awakening and transforming through thinking, feeling and willing, allows for the possibility of creating a space for the "I am" to penetrate the layers of our being and become more present in body and soul. If we can become more self-aware and oriented, more connected with our inner strength and feeling life, more able to confront difficult situations, to stay present and able to take action to express how we really feel and think—then a more genuine and authentic speaking (and expressing of oneself, not necessarily verbally) can shine through, coming from the core of our being as a creative activity. Sustainable change and transformation happen in our everyday lives and interactions, with the next person we meet as opportunities for learning, such as becoming less reactive and not avoiding or trying to please others. True soulful speaking allows us the opportunity to fulfill our destiny.

When the "I am" deepens itself in feeling, thinking can become inspired and is freed from its dependence on bodily sense perception.[25] When we learn to face and dissolve our personal fears, expose and take care of self-hatred and doubt, then we can potentially speak more truly, express feelings more honestly and become more creative human beings. It appears that change *is* happening, whether we call it a process of change, alchemy, metamorphosis or transformation, and there are new capacities being developed through a growing richness in our imagination and a more secure confidence in our intuition and knowing.

25 Steiner (2004).

We can consider the importance of including body, soul and spirit from three perspectives: in the body, we find the world as a given fact; in the soul, we make the world our own personal concern; and in the spirit, we strive for knowledge of the world.[26] The power of love, as a guiding force for the "I am" to arrive is a crucial condition that can be summarized as three qualities of soul that must be developed if we are to meet successfully the demands of the world. These are: a deep and strong interest in what we can be in the future; a strong "I am" making responsible choices as a co-creator; and the soul's need to become free to feel itself as world soul.[27] Psychophonetics is useful in this regard since it offers an experiential process for overcoming everyday reactions and owning projections by developing an awareness of what resounds within us, by listening to this inner resounding.

Change and transformation are ongoing and mean we will have to learn to work more creatively in our thinking so that doubt in spiritual things does not take over and lead us into fantasy and illusionary thinking. Fear is a common challenge for most people to face today, and with so much fighting, terrorism and uncertainty in the world, it can make us feel vulnerable to feeling attacked by negative forces, which can limit our spirit becoming more creative. However, it is as if the world is now demanding that we face our fears and develop more courage, love and hope within so we can overcome these negative influences on the astral, etheric and physical bodies.

As thinking, feeling and willing become more integrated into our whole being, there is the potential for developing more intimate relationships through a deeper listening and speaking. If the core of constructive power is speaking, then how does it affect our ability to speak and act in the world? How do we translate our learning and changes into real life situations, and does this process make us feel more separate or closer with others? This is one response from a client:

---

26 Sardello (1995).

27 Sardello (1995:xviii).

> I have compassion for that person so I would say: yes, it brings me closer to a person rather than keeping me separate from them. One lady who was being angry with me said, "Why aren't you arguing with me?" which made me laugh of course and I said, "Well, I'm allowing you to express how you feel." And that completely changed that person in themself, she realized that all she really wanted to do was express herself and sometimes we're not able to do that, and by just having the space to do that and me allowing her to do that brought her to a place where she could breathe and relax...When we don't argue it sort of stops people in their tracks and they sort of land in a soft place and sort of go, "Oohh hang on, this is different. I'm not used to having no fire. Hang on, who are you? What are you about? Why aren't you arguing with me?" So it puts me in a place that I have never visited before, and all of a sudden we're finding common ground together. That is great...so that does make it much better.

Embodying language and expressing through the whole body deepens our speaking and, through growing and developing the skills learned in counseling, this client could create something new:

> It is like having a little *handbag of skills;* they are not just in the counseling room anymore; they are day-to-day. I actually feel like I have an emergency kit for things I never had an emergency kit for before, and I am feeling that they are becoming more part of me as were the reactions and projections and the fear. These are becoming an automatic part of me and kick in anyway, they are like a first thought now rather than before it would have been to react. So there's been an osmosis of the skills coming into my body and I can actually function better for myself, and for all those that are around me as well.

Summarizing

In these three types of issues, we can see possibilities for creative ways to face fear, self-hatred and doubt of the spirit as possible ways to prevent distortions in our thinking and feeling and to allow us freely to take action in the world. By mobilizing the soul faculties of courage, love and creativity, we can learn to live with, as an act of picturing, and to encounter, the inner dimensions of life's difficulties, bringing them into our own unique perspective for growth, development and creativity.

Through consciously entering our inner life dynamics, we may enter into the *inner chamber* of a reaction, uncovering past hurt and healing and providing the resources that are really needed. For example, a young woman came to counseling with unbearable pain that became a pathway for meeting her inner needs. Through a participatory approach, she was able to heal her body. She could do this only after she had penetrated into the deep bodily memory and embedded patterns of her experience of past abuses. Through her process, the following activities became visible: she became aware and understood that the presence of past embedded memories were actually still happening in the present; she learned to stay consciously present in the body instead of leaving it or disappearing as she had done as a defense strategy to survive when she was a child; she released negative forces of abuse; she found a safe and protected area inside her body; and she was able to connect with and utilize spiritual resources to heal her body and to restore a sense of equilibrium and wholeness.

These processes offer a map for each person on the journey of soul transformation and spiritual awareness, furthering the evolution of consciousness. For instance, overcoming reactions is probably a good starting point for learning to meet others in a more meaningful and caring way, for connecting deeply with spiritual resources and for working fruitfully in the world, for creating peace among peoples.

Creative and artistic expressions are useful in sessions and can be used instead of gesturing—artistic expression is a gesture, is an expression of speaking. For instance, a client addresses her inner reactions to parenting and relationship using clay, painting and poetry to work through reactive patterns of behavior. Using these mediums can create a direct access to the living, unconscious dimensions of the human soul, and as we venture forth through life we need to remember that participating in the process of transformation is ongoing, unfinished and always changing.

These are some of the ways in which we can apply psychosophy in practice and it would take a book in itself to describe all of them. The following chapters give a more practical perspective with stories, research and insights into different topics, issues and processes.

Finally, beyond modalities and techniques, in the spirit of the meeting between two people in the counseling process and of the evolving human being, let us remember to keep finding our knowing afresh:

> We should not assume that we have already found the truth. Let us seek it together as something that none of us knows. Because we can seek for it in love and peace only if we forgo the bold assumption that we alone have found it and possess it. If, however, I cannot expect that much from you, at least allow me to listen to you and to talk with you, as with people that I do not presume to know.[28]

28 St. Augustine, in his *Contra Epistulam Manichaei* (in Wehr, 2002:260).

Part 2

Stories, Research and Insights from Practice

A PRAYER
For the Manifestation of the True Potential of Human Meeting

Yehuda Tagar

May the creation of all beings be remembered

May it be truly named

Its essence—further manifest.

And may its will prevail
As it does within the Heart of things
So also in their outer manifestations.

May our Bodies be nurtured and healed;

May our wounds transform in us into compassion
So that the pains we have inflicted ourselves might be forgiven.

And may the Pressures to be more or less than Human
Give way in us to the human being that we are,

So that from the Lie we may awaken

To our true Light

Our true Life

And our Love

(based on The Lord's Prayer)

Chapter 4

More Quickening than Light: The Surprising Gift of Conversation

Linda Hall

"Whence came you hither?" asked the golden king.
"Out of the clefts where gold dwells" replied the serpent.
"What is more glorious than gold?"
"Light!"
"What is more quickening than Light?"
"Conversation!"
—Goethe, *"The Green Snake and the Beautiful Lily"*

Goethe conceived conversation as the art of arts. This art of conversation conjures up a memory from a long time ago of an idealistic twenty-three-year-old me standing up in a room filled with a few hundred activists, my naïve idealism for all to see, almost begging them to study conscious conversation as a path toward healing the personal and political schisms among us. I did not know the first details of such a conversation myself, but I figured that we would find them together if we tried. We tried and didn't find them together, not to my knowledge anyway.

The "art of conversation" can also conjure up something else for me that is deeply nourishing and relevant to my work and, I believe, very relevant to our times, times when more and more children are becoming increasingly mute and when virtual exchanges between surrogate "avatars" are the most intimate conversations many people may experience. It is a time when intellectual debate still dominates much so-called conversation and the feeling realm is hijacked by emotionalism, prejudice and subjectivism. It is a time when the mystery of speech is so far removed from common sense that there is little common understanding about its profound creative power.

Ironically, although Psychophonetics counseling/psychotherapy may be most readily, even uniquely, identified by its work with the post-conversation action processes, I have become more and more interested in how it has enhanced my conversational work with clients. Even as Psychophonetics provides ways to work nonverbally, it has also taken the Conversational Phase of my counseling sessions to pathways of facilitation that perhaps otherwise may have remained closed to me.

My use of the word *perhaps* and the lack of substantive research to back up my supposition leave the conversation I am having with you, dear reader, quite free of strident claims and evident proofs. What follows is a description of a lifelong search for good, beautiful and true conversation, a search I shall not link to any direct origin or cause of which I can be sure, but that is a dominant theme resounding throughout my biography. I will unfold this written conversation with you as it arises from my biography, pointing to the themes of my life that are coming together, as my hindsight lengthens, toward a more coherent life story.

I am including my counseling/psychotherapy practice and the facilitating of an adult education course in Singapore, where I have lived for five years at the time of writing, introducing anthroposophic pictures to local people. I have just completed facilitating a story-telling module, which awakened in me a deeper connection to storytelling than I have had before. I am thinking and feeling in stories even more than before, and this chapter is shaped accordingly. As I write the pictures appear, of people and places in my Psychophonetics history.

I have, at different challenging times in my life, experienced a great need for a particular quality of conversation. Looking back, I can see how desperately I clung to it during those times, as to a lifeline, sure that I would drown in the horrendous, stormy, dark depths of my emotional life if I could not find that safe harbor, a sympathetic ear. The sad and confusing stories of my life experiences filled me, and I needed someone to be a listener. In hindsight, I can see that they were essentially stories about fears, self-doubt and self-hate, which Steiner calls the Three Beasts, as being those powers that challenge us to overcome and rise above them. At the time, they were simply my personal horror stories about unrequited love, abandonment, lifecycle challenges, vocational confusion, insecurities, addictions and attachments, and other jetsam and flotsam of my life that loomed iceberg-like in front of my seemingly fragile little life boat, threatening to capsize me.

I came to counseling and psychotherapy gradually, throughout years of experiencing various modalities as a client. By the time I reached my thirties I was still seeking something I did not know existed, but I knew for certain by then it was of a "transpersonal" nature and I had become alert to the danger of giving one's power over to a healer or healing method. The story of Goethe's *Faust* resonated with me as: what if I gave away my soul for the sake of "recovering" my idea of wholeness?

I had originally enrolled in a transpersonally oriented counseling course hoping to learn how to apply the approach to myself, but after a few years of part-time study, I started to imagine that I could become a practitioner. It was the "wounded healer" story, except that I had no desire to be seen as a "healer" or to "heal." However, the word *facilitator* appealed to me then and still does. It was in a training session in this course in 1989, when I had my first meeting with Yehuda Tagar and Philophonetics, as it was known then, where he was a guest speaker and completely unknown to me. When I saw my first demonstration of this approach, I saw something of which I had only dreamed. I saw a potential for me to work creatively and nonverbally in a way that empowers the client in the therapeutic relationship.

The training in Psychophonetics that followed and the years of counseling since, I have been sobered, thankfully, by research that humbles counselors who think too highly of their particular modality. If the research is true, then the main factors that have the most therapeutic impact are: what the client brings to the therapy room; the nature of the "therapeutic alliance" and the "placebo–hope–expectancy" factors. The modality itself mainly bore weight to the degree it facilitated these others.

In light of this and the respect it shows the client, I have concluded to date that the Psychophonetics approach as I apply it is enhancing my ability to co-create a therapeutic alliance that is beneficial and enables me to facilitate a process that is effective. I do not insist that it is the best process for all clients but rather feel that, amongst other things, it has a great deal to offer in facilitating quality therapeutic alliances and in taking conversation to a much deeper potential for visualization (pictorial imagination) for the client and counselor.

It is the *potential* of Psychophonetics to empower clients in their engagement with the counselor that I respond to. It is the potential of Psychophonetics to facilitate counseling increasingly toward freedom for the client and me that first drew me to train as a practitioner. This claim is difficult to substantiate, of course. How can I test it against such variables as my own development over time in regard to my intuition and insight as a counselor, development that may have happened anyway? I cannot. I can only tell the story and sense into the difference I feel this approach has made to my work.

However, it is not only Psychophonetics, as this training also brought me to the work of Rudolf Steiner and Anthroposophy. While studying, I woke up to the presence of a very deep source of wisdom underpinning this approach. When I discovered that the primary source and its roots are in Steiner's book *Speech and Drama* and his lectures on psychosophy, I became an avid reader of Steiner's work.

My already keen interest in conversation was nourished by studies of Anthroposophy, most notably in a little book about Goethean conversation by Marjorie Spock. Although I have only ever experienced this form of group conversation a few times in study groups, it has stayed with me as a beacon of light. I recognized something in it for which my soul longs. That light still beckons, and I still seek people with whom to explore a Goethean conversation, but more about Goethean conversation later.

It is the inner pictures evoked out of Psychophonetics and the resultant possibility of the action work that give foundation to the counseling conversation I engage in with clients. Ironically, this can at times take the conversational counseling to a level of picture-making within me and the client that makes the action work less central. The "movement from stuckness into breathing" is often facilitated by the picture-making that evolves out of the conversation alone. It is as if an expansion takes place within the client as a result of our conversational picture-making and an ability to breathe more deeply is acquired, with a remembered and renewed ability to digest the concerns that brought the client to counseling.

Focus on the conversation phase is more important, particularly with a client from a culture where professional one-to-one counseling is not an assumed resource. In some cultures, there are factors that make such counseling strange, even taboo. In a place such as Singapore where East and West meet in very dynamic and paradoxical ways, I find my counseling straddling at least two worlds when I work with the local people, such as those of Chinese and Indian heritage.

Of course, there can be no cultural generalizations about these clients, but I offer examples of some issues that can arise out of certain cultural assumptions where:

- What happens within the family stays within the family. Shame is to be avoided at all cost. For example, the need to "save face" means that a "problem" or an abuse must be hidden, or is totally denied since the idea of individual rights is not assumed.
- Religious or secular or family elders are the supposed sources of advice and family law. For example, to see a counselor would be a terrible insult to the authority figure of the family.
- Filial piety is placed above personal freedoms. For example, questions of personal choice are not even negotiable. One obeys or is judged as disobedient or egoistic in some way.

- Privacy of feelings is considered paramount to civility and good manners. For example, the public airing of feelings or experiences (even in a counseling session) would be viewed as a weakness of character, at least.
- Bodily expression is confined or prescribed, and free expression even in the arts is considered a lack of good taste, for example, where dance is a set form passed down through the ages, not a chance to express oneself...where individual expressive movement is not a part of everyday life. Gestures and movement in ordinary life are limited to cultural norms and forms.
- Behaviors in relationships are defined and given as fixed according to caste, gender, age, wealth, status, religion, place of birth or residence, race and so on. For example, an arranged marriage that does not please the bride is not viewed as a cause for the woman to seek counseling, but a blessing for which the woman should be grateful.
- Religious practice, such as meditation, is assumed to solve all inner conflict. For example, I have Buddhist clients who feel that they are failing their practice by coming to a counselor: "My teacher tells me that if I only meditated more I would not have this problem."

As I offer this list I am reminded again that there is nothing about my experiences of counseling Caucasian Anglo-Saxons in Australia that would suggest that Psychophonetics action work is generally more suitable there than in Singapore. I do not counsel cultures. I counsel individuals with diverse cultural relationships. I have worked with Caucasians with less readiness around movement and sound work than some of my Asian clients. But this is not to deny that counseling as I know it is a relatively new industry in Asia as compared to the cities in Australia. While this may affect the numbers of prospective clients I have in Singapore, it does not determine the experience I will have with each client. That remains as unique and mysterious with each of them whether in Asia or in Australia.

It is with the first tender explorations of conversation with a client that I begin to meet the "other," whether it is the otherness of their individuality, their race, their gender, their religion, their circumstances, or their "wish."[1] This dance of conversation needs a deep sensitivity and true interest, a standard toward which I can only keep aspiring, particularly with those whose first language is other than English. It is with conversation where I first invite participation and demonstrate my intention of "presence."

Just as Steiner-inspired storytelling offers to awaken images within the soul of the listener, so does the Psychophonetics counseling conversation. As the client speaks, I surrender any intellectual analysis to the deeper wisdom of the images that grow like a pictorial story within. With the client's prior agreement, I usually draw Mind Maps[2] as the client's story unfolds. It keeps me focused and away from any tendency to theorize. When a "theory" presents itself—it can be in words or feelings or pictures, as if out of the blue—I simply make a quick note on the Mind Map with my initials to distinguish it from the client's words, and return to recording the story. Many clients have told me that they really love the feeling of being recorded so actively in Mind Maps, they say they feel more deeply listened to than even eye contact can sometimes convey, and they can see that I am not sitting back making theories in my head and nodding enigmatically as if I either understand them or have a secret understanding more true than their own. Mind Mapping seems to demonstrate this "presence" more so than would a linear scribing, as the pictorial nature of a Mind Map shows pictures and links and attempts at a deeper understanding, whereas linear note-taking appears to demonstrate that I can take down what is being said.

---

1 The "wish" is the Psychophonetics term for clients' statements about what they specifically choose to explore in the session, made after the *Common Picture* is affirmed.

2 See books on mind maps by Tony Buzan. Website: www.buzan.com.au/products/index.html.

In this process I am actively engaged with the client in the usual conversational skills that draw out, challenge, and focus, in the familiar ways of facilitating verbal exchanges in counseling. I "listen" to the breathing within the telling, and within the story: moments of expansion and contraction. I listen for when it is time to offer back the story to the client, in my own pictures, to ascertain whether I have stayed on the same journey with them or gone off into some abstract byway of my own theorizing and lost their trail. My first task is to see their story through their eyes. Any insights of my own have been noted on the Mind Map and may or may not be brought to light. When people ask how it is that I do not feel burnt out at the end of a day of counseling, I point to this practice as one of the factors and to the following aspects being engaged with while facilitating the Conversational Phase:

- Inwardly evoke the presence of the spiritual world to be with me.
- Listen to clients' stories from their point of view and record them on Mind Maps.
- Make a note of any of my own pictures/theories/thoughts/feelings/questions as they arise, and initial them to distinguish them as mine.
- Utilize verbal counseling skills to facilitate clients to tell their stories as richly and deeply and subtly as they are ready to do.
- Inwardly await the moment when I sense it is time to offer back their pictures, so as to get their agreement that I have stayed close to their stories as they see them.

If I have facilitated the above, then the client and I experience a particularly sacred moment: the attainment of the Common Picture, which is the Psychophonetics term for the resonance between client and counselor regarding their picture of the client's issue and inner dynamics. There has been no focus on strategy yet or solutions, just the client's story and any attached feelings and emotions, and an openness to connecting with the highest possibility through being in a state of presence, allowing the future to arrive.

Sometimes it can take nearly a whole session to come to a Common Picture and there can also be moments of a profoundly reverential ambience created by the arrival of the Common Picture in such sessions: as if a deep breath had been taken, or a deep exhalation, leaving only awe, reverence or wonder. Clients can come back to a following session with a completely changed story, telling me that because of the way they were able to tell their story and because of the way their story was received with freedom, support and reverence, they could digest it for the first time and spontaneously move into an even deeper, or truer, or more relevant story, or deeper question, or even an insight. For some clients the opportunity for such a storytelling was the actual need they came with, unbeknownst even to themselves at the time, bringing a felt inner movement with which they were content to be for awhile, requiring no immediate follow-up session.

Pictorial imagination is threatened with extinction in our times, as media creates and pours other peoples' processed and packaged images into our living rooms. Children are as likely to see the movie before they have read the book, and so even reading, which once left something to the imagination, is often now interpreted for us first by the filmmaker. While children are best nourished in their early years by their natural, dreamlike pictorial imagination, this ability is sorely threatened by the developing intellectuality of later childhood and then adult life. While the thinking faculties need to be awakened as we approach adulthood, premature awakening and imbalanced intellectuality can make disembodied "talk therapy" a closed circuit of supposition, analysis, theorizing and fantasy. The artistic and action therapies aim to break this closed circuit by appealing to the ability of humans to engage with their pictorial imagination and hold "conversations of the psyche" without dependence upon the words around which the intellect weaves its self-talk.

So, it has been with some surprise that I have found myself working to such an extent with verbal conversation with clients. It is only because I can see that their pictorial imagination is being awakened through the conversation that I am able to embrace it. It is this pictorial imagination that supports the "visualization" that is the essential guide for the action work aspect of Psychophonetics. Without the visualization, the client could become stuck on the circuit of theory, analysis and fantasy. The coming to a Common Picture between client and counselor would be dry and lifeless. The name "Common Picture" suggests an experience that is more pictorial than mere "ideas." Pictorial imagination has the potential to liberate the client and counselor from reducing the issue into a matter of assumed "cause and effect": I feel and behave like this because this event happened to me. Out of the pictures themes emerge. The client's story becomes a bridge for the soul, uniting the world of imagination to the world of thinking, potentially cooperative worlds increasingly divided by the abyss created by the over-intellectualization of our times. When this bridge is created by the story being told and received in a way that awakens pictorial imagination, then "living thinking" can thrive: the kind of thinking that sees the world as more than the sum of its parts. Only when the world is viewed in such a way can true understanding occur.

Such imaginative thinking prepares the way for the blooming of intuitive perception. Mere sensory observation and intellectual perception lead us only into the debating room, where conflicting, concrete, so-called facts are hurled from side to side: a debate of theories, analyses, prejudices, fabricated laws and morals, stereotypes, opinions and idealisms. If we are overly habituated to discussion then we can hardly conceive of higher levels of conversation.[3]

This is the quandary of the client, whose own inner landscape is often the scene for such circular and repetitive debate. Out of this circuitous debate little awakened understanding or insight can come, but only quarrelling inner opinions or even despair. Sometimes I sense that clients come to counseling unconsciously or consciously looking for an adjudicator. How I manage not to become this adjudicator while facili-

3 Spock (1983:9).

tating a therapeutic conversation is largely an unfolding mystery to me still. However, I offer these insights:

- Knowing that the Conversational Phase is a veil over insights that lie deeper than words and are accessible only through an intuitive act requires a different approach. I listen differently, probe differently and challenge differently.
- A quality of silence is allowed to develop throughout the client's "storytelling" and ensuring conversation, so that "words for words'" sake don't become disturbers of the peace, destroying our sense of inner quiet and the development of our intuitive capacities.[4]
- Suspend inner chatter as the clients offer their stories, and while listening, allow only pictures to come intuitively. Many clients have told me that Mind Mapping has facilitated their storytelling greatly, as it is an outward sign of inner attention, uninterrupted attention they often have never experienced before. Some have said that by my scribing their story it assures them that I am not sitting there thinking opinions and theorizing about them, but that I am focused only upon their picture of their story. It affirms for them very literally that I am doing client-focused counseling. They sense that my "picture," offered only after their story is fully spent, must be deeply informed by their picture, since it is clearly where I have been devoting all of my attention.
- Intentionally "sacrifice" thinking, sensing, and picturing to the pictures "painted" with the clients' words, their natural bodily gestures made as they speak, their breathing and with the sounds that accompany their words. This can be a happy sacrifice and is also a blessing, as it is the best way I have found to digest the suffering expressed in these stories. Only by being fully with the client do I maintain my immunity to being overwhelmed by

4 Spock (1983:6).

the suffering within it, or by my own reactions to it, and to any potential burden I could be tempted to take on as a facilitator.

I have had the privilege of working with clients who have come with a long-term intention: to use the counseling sessions as a way to practice self-reflection and spiritual development, not only to address chronic or critical issues of concern. These clients have often voluntarily reported that the conversations we have shared over time have trained them to deepen their ability to think in pictures themselves in their everyday lives. For example, one client reports that she is increasingly able to picture inwardly, both backward to a moment when a feeling was bypassed and a reaction took over, and forward to potential reactions she can sense arising in the future as a result of feelings to which she is currently slow to awaken. As a result of this deepening sensing and visualizing/picturing she is finding that her relationship to both past and future is more and more available to her response ability. The once overwhelming effect of fears, self-doubts and self-hatred is giving way to her growing "immunity." It is particularly pertinent, regarding the topic of this chapter, that this client and I now do counseling over the phone as she moved overseas some time ago, but maintains my services while she transitions into a new personal and therapeutic community. Because of her move, I have not been able to utilize the action work of Psychophonetics with her since she left Singapore. The conversational work that we developed in our face-to-face sessions to a very imaginative level alongside the action work now continues to develop over the phone. In a recent phone session she described with great detail exactly how her body was responding to the pictures we were sharing arising from her "storytelling." While I would not suggest she is doing Psychophonetics to herself, and would not recommend that anyway, her access to the feeling life within via her bodily responses was a source of much confirmation, clarification and guidance for both of us.

Other clients have told me that they have learned from our conversational work in sessions how to "see pictures" more than they were able to before, when their intellectual inner debate would have kept them arguing from side to side. These spontaneous pictures help to quiet the meaningless "chatter" and become inspiring guides. When I receive this feedback, I recall that the purpose of Goethean conversation is to call forth a fullness of spiritual life, with thoughts as intuitions, whereas if we engage in just mental, intellectual conversation we may end up feeling unfulfilled and isolated.[5]

True conversations have the power to overcome such isolation and, as we strive to enter the world of living thoughts together, we can each attune our intuitive perception by being open and receptive and through attentive listening. In this mood, a sense of presence can be strengthened. The art of listening is a spiritual act connecting listener, teller and spirit, and by listening deeply to one another with reverence and no reaction, our soul becomes available for inspired creativity.[6]

These words echo in my ears every time I sit with a client and begin to listen. The form of conversation with a client will be different from that used in a Goethean conversation group, but the intention resonates. Conversation that aspires to what Steiner calls living thinking, with the awakening of true inner feeling, can call to imagination and bring it back to us, to make us truly human.

The action elements of Psychophonetics counseling offer to build a bridge between thinking and imagination and pave a way to the client's intuition. It is my growing experience that the conversation that precedes and accompanies the action work can become far more than a secondary facilitator to the action work. When inspired by artistic principles, the client–counselor conversation can of itself become a pathway that facilitates a growing freedom for clients and their capacity for spiritual self-activity.

My experience of the conversational phase of counseling has confirmed that to achieve true conversations one must, in short, build with the material of intuition, and to reach this height everything of a per-

5 Spock (1983).

6 Spock (1983: 2–3).

sonal, sentient nature must be sacrificed and only then can a conversation find its way to necessity and become a conversation with the spiritual world as well as with our fellow human beings. We need to remain awake to the importance and healing power of an in-depth conversation in itself as well as its importance when continuing into an action phase.

The following is an email received from an adult participant enrolled in one of the courses I facilitate. When I recall the conversation to which she refers I remember being very present, giving my full attention, and listening deeply. It is fitting that the last words of this chapter come from a client:

> I could not sleep after our conversation on Saturday about my difficulty with [a situation]...I was reflecting and consolidating my energy for staying with this phase of [the situation]...which felt like eternity to me...and next thing I know [she describes a sudden insight and change of perspective]...What a break this is for me. Actually I feel a great shift of energy after speaking with you. What seems stuck flowed again [the conversation]; it gave me clarity to get back on the path and the strength to stay in it with my [situation].

Chapter 5

Cancer as a Threshold of Inner Healing: Clare's Journey

Yehuda Tagar

Editor's introduction: A number of high-profile women in Australia have been diagnosed with cancer in recent years, such as Belinda Emmett, Jane McGrath, the Olympic runner Kerryn McCann, and others. These women have helped to highlight how we as a society deal with illness and death, and how we can learn to see these women and others as being on a journey of "living with cancer" rather than seeing cancer as a battleground in which they have to survive and have to "beat the cancer." A question we can ask is: What have these women and others taught us? What can we all learn from these women? They became public examples of how to live better, showing us that their spirit is strong, and how their presence in life and their passing inspires us.

Ian Gawler is another inspiring person who lived through the experience of cancer, but in his case, he did not die. Instead, he set up a healing center for people who wish to make changes in their life. Out of his journey of trying many forms of healing, he developed programs and services for healing and wellness, including meditation, nutrition, counseling and spiritual care. In a talk given by Ian Gawler,[1] he told how thirty-five people who had lived with cancer for a long time were surveyed and asked to rank in level of importance the range of things they had done that helped. He said most people claimed that a wide

1 Gawler (2008).

range of things were important, and when asked to choose the three most important things that helped, they chose diet, stillness of meditation, and having a spiritual life. Gawler went on to quote Gabriel Kune, Emeritus Professor of Surgery at Melbourne University, and editor of the book *The Psyche and Cancer,* in which Kune describes four special characteristics of people who have lived through "advanced malignancy" and who are still living:

- Seek a wide exposure to conventional medical opinion and treatment
- Seek also a wide exposure to non-conventional opinion and treatment
- Operate at an intuitive level
- Are at peace with themselves

In another study, the following characteristics were found to be associated with people whose cancer had unexpectedly regressed and who were still living:

> A strong sense of self-sufficiency, competency and control; living a fulfilling and enjoyable life, beyond the crisis of cancer; having at least one strong, supportive and trusted relationship; being comfortable with the expression of both positive and negative emotions; finding meaning in the cancer experience and accepting the diagnosis but not the prognosis; working in partnership with health professionals and participating in decisions related to their health and wellbeing; regular participation in activities and practices that reduce stress; having a sense of spiritual connection or awareness; and flexibility and the willingness to try new things and/or make changes when something is no longer working.[2]

Counseling can be an important factor in this healing process and in striving toward a life well lived, as forty-year-old Anna Cole comments: "I'm glad I had cancer, and I would have it again because I have learned that (otherwise) you would not have come to this point

2 Dye (2008: para. 8) describes research by Schiltz and IONS from 2004.

in life where I know exactly why we are here and our purpose." Anna described this "point in life" as a state of unconditional love, and her family described it as an awakening. Previously, Anna had no interest in spiritual matters and had spent her life as a peacemaker by smoothing things over for others, but not expressing how she really felt at the time. Anna then had a number of Psychophonetics counseling sessions to deal with issues she said had been held in for over twenty years, and stated it was one of her regrets that she had not done this sooner:

"If I had been able to deal with all those things stuffed up inside me, they would not have manifested themselves."[3] Anna has since crossed the threshold of death. In this chapter, Yehuda Tagar describes in detail an inspiring case study about Clare's therapeutic journey of living with cancer,[4] which also exemplifies some of the above-mentioned research findings.

Clare's Journey

Cancer is not only a crossroad of bodily health, it is also a crossroad of consciousness, a threshold between being identified with the outer dimension of existence into awakening to oneself as an inner being and awakening to one's journey as an inner one, of which the bodily one is but one aspect. In my clinical work as a counselor, I have accompanied people many times across this threshold of awareness. It is for me a deep privilege to be there in such moments, as they are powerful reminders of the essence, the beauty and the dignity of being human. The moment of awakening, when the human soul finds its inner identity in spite of and because of the bodily condition, embracing the body rather than being embraced by it, is a great moment of inner victory and of freedom.

Psychophonetics is a path of awakening to one's inner resources with the help of the nonverbal dimensions of intelligence, such as sensa-

---

3 Lahey (1993:3).

4 Clare's story was originally published in a conference paper (1996), "The Healing Power of Expression: Cancer as a Threshold of Inner Healing," in Ian Gawler (ed.). *The Mind–Body Connection Conference Proceedings* (reprinted here with permission).

tion, visualization, movement, and sound. It provides, at any phase of one's physical wellbeing, a range of tools for such a transition, helping to access the reality of the inner life and to enter it actively, beyond the limitations of intellectual, verbal communication. In this chapter, I wish to share the insight, beauty and power of a process with Clare as she went through five counseling sessions in the final stages of her life.

Session 1: Clare was in an advanced stage of cancer when I first saw her and she realized that the chemotherapy had not worked, that she had only a few months to live, and she was tired of the losing struggle of survival. Now at fifty years old, Clare states: "There must be more than survival," which is her first powerful statement to me in a counseling session, one of many arising out of unfathomable depths of soul, triggered to become conscious by the strange alchemy of facing the threshold of death.

Many professionals, friends and relatives were surrounding her with their concern for therapy, cure, and minimizing her suffering. Clare was quietly developing another agenda: "I have to unlearn many ways of surviving. It is time to face them and to clear myself from the past." For this, she came for counseling. The past was haunting her and she had a sense of urgency in her wish to let go in time. She felt she was not allowed to develop a sense of identity as a child, or be appreciated for who she genuinely is, so learned to survive without expressing her uniqueness. This habit lingered into later years, covering her true essence but now it is no longer okay to put up with this habitual cover.

Out of all that could be wished by a terminally ill person, her stated wish is: "I want to get in touch with my true self, to find a voice to express it. Something needs to be retrieved from many years of being crushed." We first turn our attention to her bodily experience. Clare feels she has been *split from her body* for many years. We allow the body to express its inner experience in its own way: sensing, movement and posture. In translating her bodily sensation into gesture rather than into words, the body's experience can speak directly to her attentive mind. She translates her experience as "I feel in need of nurturing; something is starved inside of me, inside my belly." She then lets go of her crouched position, shakes it off, and focuses her attention on the core of that starvation. Encouraged, she enters in gesture into that experience, becoming the experience of starvation. The focus shifts to the heart. On exiting from that position and reflecting on it, Clare knows that it is her heart, hidden in her stomach, which has been starved for love from very early on. She has been cut off from heart nourishment.

We enter a process of *enlivening* that supports the circulation of the body's life energy with movement, breathing, gesture and sounds. She moves gently every movable part of her body, spontaneously, effortlessly, and her warmth increases. She notices tension in her shoulders and in the belly. The tension is expressed in gesture, tightened further with an intake of breath and is released in gesture, movement and sounds. Her warmth increases further. By being more aware of the life dynamics in these parts, she can express their inner needs: "to be nurtured, to be soothed and protected." Now that the tension is released, there is an openness to receive support. Sounds are discovered which can address these needs: "*MMM*" in a deep tone, a soothing "*SHHH,*" a sheltering "*HUBBB.*" Her body receives these sound vibrations with enjoyment and relief expressed in gesture and movement, and the "enlivening" process is completed. She feels warm, accommodated, relaxed and consoled. The loving presence of her husband who accompanied her in the session secures the maintenance of this atmosphere around her as they depart. There is light in her face.

Session 2: A week later Clare reports that she has managed to practice some "enlivening" successfully at home. On the medical front intense treatments are taking their toll, but Clare can distinguish between what is not in her hands and what is. Now she is eager to get on with her inner agenda. There is a big issue from the past she wants to clear—guilt: "Guilt is eating me up." She can identify a constant voice telling her that she has no rights. As she speaks this, a great tiredness comes upon her and she has to lie down. All her energy is sapped away, as if her forces are draining down into a black hole in her belly and her instinct is to run away from it into her head: "I cannot be in my belly because it is too gloomy there," she says. There in the head she knows what to do: "My rational mind is a great escape. That is what I have always done."

Then she acknowledges that the part of herself that is locked away in the belly, surrounded by judgment and guilt, is still stuck there, depleting her vitality and clarity. She makes a choice to override the instinctive escape and to enter the "gloomy place" in the belly, where there is a need for healing. Clare knows that only she can consciously perform that healing, and she takes responsibility for doing this. She relaxes into and comes to rest within the gloomy, dark place in her belly. It is not as frightening as she thinks. She can breathe and finds there a great need for gentle warmth. The sound "*FFF*" spoken gently brings the desired warmth into the belly. She breathes in with that quality and then breathes out expressing a warm, soft, gentle blue "*FFFlame*" of "*FFF.*" In her active, spontaneous visualization, the colors in her belly change from dark blue into green, which becomes more and more a golden green. Light and warmth spread inside her belly. Her energy returns and so does her joy. Then it becomes safe enough to be conscious of the source of that gloom. It comes naturally and spontaneously. She remembers being about two years old in a refugee camp after the war and being isolated from her mother for two weeks, and since then has experienced depression. These early memories are of no warmth, no connectedness to mother, and an abyss of unexpressed sadness.

Clare is invited to invoke the energy and the presence of the mother she never had, but always longed for. She does this easily, but something in her heart is blocking access to this imagined nurturing energy. She becomes the heart in gesture, sensing, feeling and gesturing its inner experience. She feels and then sees pieces of icy broken glass stuck in it, which are blocking the access of warmth to her inner being. It is enough for her to see this for now and we close the process. Her tasks until the next session are to enhance her connection to the inner mother energies she discovered in herself during the session and to come to know more about these pieces of glass. This is the most difficult end of session we had.

Session 3: When Clare comes to the next session within a week, she knows exactly what persons in her life represented these icy pieces of broken glass. She can name them, she can make the connection between outer biographical events and patterns and that metaphor, and she is ready for a big clearing job. Her wish is finally to be rid of these influences and then, to heal her heart, the seat of her real self. We start the action phase of the session by restoring in memory and in sensation the experience of the "inner mother" nurturing energies that she invoked in the previous session: "*MMM*" and "*FFF*" and sounding them well.

Then through entering in sensing, gesture and visualization, the map of the debilitating pattern is drawn up and becomes visible. Fortresses of fear are guarding the way to her wounds. There is fear in the stomach; there is devastation in the heart sheath. Clare becomes in gesture the fortresses of fear, speaking their aggressive sound: a blocked *GGG*. In the heart, they transform into arrows of broken glass with the gesture and sound of a piercing *T*. Clare sounds, gestures, and when she is ready, she uses the same forces to get these energies out of her heart sheath, one by one. It is a painful operation with no physical instruments, like open flesh and knives, but in pure images, sensations and sounds. This action clears the poisonous energies, allowing warmth and healing to enter and to do their work.

The connection is made and Clare can now bring warmth to bear on her heart, as the pieces of glass melt away, the invoked mother's warmth can reach it. The love, warmth and compassion that Clare has given to others all her life is now available to her inner being, which had been cut off by coldness, judgment and the contraction of guilt. The "inner mother" energy is intense and is reaching her with the help of a combination of the sounds "*FFFF*" and "*MMM*" spoken rhythmically, softly, mediated by the round, reassuring sound of O. Something deep is being healed, consoled and embraced. Guilt has no hold and real forgiveness can now be imagined. Clare leaves the session feeling as if a huge weight has lifted off her whole being.

Session 4: A few weeks pass by. Clare's physical conditions deteriorate further to a degree that prevents her from coming to the clinic any more. The next session takes place at her bedside. She is physically very frail and hardly capable of movement, but clear and alert in her mind, and determined to complete the clearing work, as she describes it. She tells me that there is some inner poison still in her, there is a residue of very early sexual abuse that she has not felt strong and safe enough to revisit, tackle and heal. However, she is determined not to go with this pollution still stuck in her. She wants to reach it, clear it, release it and then complete the forgiveness to the person concerned, who has been among the dead for many years. She does not want to take this baggage with her to the other side. It is clear between us that this is not the time for great external action in the mold of the past few sessions. On the other hand, there is no need for it. The process of conversing and taking hold of the inner, subtle realities is now very familiar to Clare. We can do it all in sensing and visualization.

Step-by-step, in a precise, common, dynamic visualization, communicated by very few words, we create a pathway for the poisonous residues of the old abuse to be released out of her system. She does not need to confront or sort out her relationship with this person anymore, as this was finished. Now there is an inner cleansing to complete, an inner washing of her life body. She finds the inner pool of dark sediment in her life body around her heart and she leads it gently, like an inner detoxification of foreign liquids, down her body into a place in her lower back that has, in her inner experience, an exit in it. From there and without resistance the dark, poisonous sedimentation of the inner pollution she has been carrying for most of her life can leave her body. A great relief registers in her face when this process is completed.

A gentle wafting of the sound "*SHHH*" is accompanied by the faintest of movements with her arm the only physical movement she did during the session completes the process. She is relaxed, content and very tired. She is almost asleep by the time I leave the room.

Session 5: The fifth and last session is a check-up session, initiated in the previous meeting. She is crossing a threshold slowly and surely, with a deep peace of mind. Her earthly business is done and completed. Physical pain does not reach her anymore. There is no irritation, complaint or desire, apart from the wish to be left in peace. All this is exchanged between us with a few words and eye contact. There is a presence of great and solid peace in the room, a sense of dignity, solemnity and clarity. I have only one question to ask her: "Are you in the space in which you wish to be?" Clare softly answers: "Yes," with a gentle light in her eyes. She is as ready as I can imagine a person near death to be. We part simply, as if we are going to meet again within a week. We both know we will not and this is okay.

Three weeks later, Clare passed away peacefully on her further soul journey.

Conclusion

It was not the task, responsibility or intention to cure Clare, but rather her task was to heal her relationship to herself, to her biography, to the people with whom she had close relationships, and to her life on Earth. Two processes were going on at the same time: the deterioration of the physical body toward its inevitable disintegration and the emergence of the inner being of Clare, for whom the process of disease was a major opportunity for awaking, for the righting and for the healing that she was not capable of accomplishing through her previous, physically healthier condition.

The illness and the dying processes are two of many phases in the soul's journey, not the end of it. This is not a belief system, but rather it is the articulation of the direct experience of the counselor and the client in the above process. The disintegration of the body is a fact. The disintegration of the inner being is not a fact, but only so many people's assumption underlying unacknowledged fear. In fact, the reverse is clearly discernible for an unbiased observation: a phase is being accomplished with the result of a greater integration and strengthening of one's inner life, triggered and strangely supported by the unique condition of being terminally ill and dying. One is left in awe at the magnitude of the process.

The unique inner wisdom, inner light, intense sanity and powerful inner beauty is bursting forth from the disintegrating boundaries of the body as from a prison. The soul is becoming visible to the observer and accessible to the consciousness of the individual, very often for the first time in one's life. Death is overcome as dying becomes yet another step in the soul's journey for wholeness.

Chapter 6

The Inner Dimensions of Parenting and Self-parenting

Robin Steele

The definition of *parent* is "parer," to bring forth and "ent," agent, forming. Parenting is about bringing forth and forming relationships with partners, children and other family members. Relationships are not a luxury or an add-on, they are essential for survival. For instance, a newborn baby has an innate and overwhelming capacity to relate. Relationships are at the very core of development and life and are especially crucial in developing families.

Parenting is a journey of the heart—of developing new capacities for relationship, as our children are not passive objects but partners in life. Raising children can be a joy and a challenge that offers the possibility to learn from our children through active observation and participation. Parenting offers many opportunities, for not only having to face and address issues happening in the outer environment around us but also for facing and coping with the variety of unresolved feelings and unwanted reactionary behaviors that may emerge within us as part of living with others. These inner reactions are part of the journey of developing the freedom to choose how we would really like to behave, to bring forth and form ourselves and our children into the human beings we can become. The consequence of overreacting is that we can affect the people around us in negative ways. It seems at times we can behave more like a child than as an adult. These layers of ourselves are now waiting for us as the adult to take notice of unresolved experiences, to take on the job of being a parent of our own inner life as a starting point for parenting others.

How can we find practical ways to become the parent we want to be with the children in our care, whether they are our own or others, and how can we maintain our sense of sanity and wellbeing as we go on this journey of parenting a future generation of adults/parents? How can we do this without letting emotions and judgments be more in control of our behavior than we wish them to be? How can we heal unresolved hurts and be more in charge of how we behave, so we can together be more hopeful and encouraging, not just for others, but also for ourselves?

Emotional Literacy

We need to accept the responsibility of self-parenting, of dealing with our own unresolved issues. Our children need us to help them find different ways of coping in this quickly changing society, with its increasing pressures on the individual and with many past ways not necessarily as relevant now. In many cultures, there are new ways of relating emerging that require new capacities, based more on the free choice of the individuals or families concerned, with clear communication skills so we can better understand others from their point of view. We are at a stage in history where there is constant change and movement, with very little in the outer world today that is secure or predictable. However, a secure foundation must still be built so that families can be encouraging, respecting each other in their uniqueness and finding creative ways to deal with life's issues.

This foundation has to be built on the inside now. Parenting is demanding us to become more intimate with our children and with ourselves, to understand the language of a soul journey. This language includes developing our heart, our feelings, how we express and take care of ourselves and each other as the basis for learning, relating with others and doing things in the world. Feelings are what bind or separate us in relationships as feelings connect or disconnect us with each other and influence close or distant friendships.

From my work as an early-childhood teacher, parent educator and as a psychotherapist working with children and parents, the greatest and most sustainable changes or improvements in families have been when the parent/s have taken responsibility for looking at their own experiences and learning how to better understand themselves as the basis for encouraging their children. This becomes a very empowering exercise for parents to experience the idea that we can no longer force others to change, but if we understand and develop ourselves by changing the way we respond rather than blindly reacting, then this automatically can affect others and change the dynamics of relationships.

It needs to be said that the significant events in parents' lives such as separation, transitions, loss and abuse, are not in themselves significant in terms of leading to difficulties in relationship. More important is the way in which we as parents have dealt with our experiences. This is what will make the difference. If we have learned to face difficulties and not avoid them, found the help we needed or were able to understand what happened and could contain this experience, then this is what potentially gives relationships a depth of understanding, self-knowledge, and a sense of truth. We can see that gaining support at critical stages in parents' and children's lives is vital and what a difference this can make to traumatic and abusive experiences.

Five aspects of emotional intelligence have been identified and developed as the heart of parenting emotionally intelligent children.[1] These aspects include the ability to know our own emotions, managing our emotions, self-motivation to contain emotions in order to reach important goals, recognizing emotions in others, and handling relationships.

I propose that our issues are not just personal ones; they belong in the world as part of what the world is calling us to develop as new

1 Goleman (1995) identifies five aspects of emotional intelligence, which Gottman (1997) developed further as the heart of parenting emotionally intelligent children.

capacities. Therefore, we can take this idea further in the development of the two sides of relationship between outer parenting and inner self-parenting. Outer parenting relates to the outer environmental and social situation and how we communicate and relate with our family and others. Inner parenting is about our relationship with ourselves, where we can change, the power of this and its effect on outer relationships. For example, the "power of one" person who develops new capacities for changing within, takes responsibility by not blaming others and understands differences can powerfully affect the whole family as a learning experience.

Other parenting approaches[2] utilize the emotional aspects of children's misbehavior and parents' responses to this as a source for awareness and parenting skills development. This information can also be an entry point into dealing with the inner self-parenting issues triggered by a child, as a basis for better parenting of one's own children (see table).

Who are the inner children? How do we recognize them? The inner aspects are part of our everyday lives in the present and can also influence our future. They are not somewhere in the past; they live within us in the present as means of coping, of surviving difficulties. They make themselves known and come to expression through the body—in the angry knot in the stomach, in the withdrawal from facing some fearful confrontation or in the sudden angry outburst, or when we behave in ways we really don't like as an adult/parent ("that wasn't me" type of feeling); becoming vague, numb, needy, embarrassed, judging, victimized, manipulative, or compromising.[3] Often these expressions appear in the repetition of unwanted behaviors that are just like those of our own parents. Most important of all, our own children often trigger in us aspects of a similar age in our memories, causing us to behave in ways we don't really want to behave until we do something to develop new ways to change these reactionary behaviors (refer to the table opposite for possible ways).

2 Dinkmeyer et al. (1989) and Balson (1988).

3 Tagar (1996b).

Table 1: Four types of children's misbehavior and capacities to be developed

Child's behaviors	Attention-seeking defending behaviors	Power	Revenge	Escape by withdrawal
Examples of behaviors	Teasing, annoying behaviors; wants to be noticed; doubts he/she is okay	Bullying; "I can do whatever I like." Covering feelings of powerlessness	"I will get even." Feeling deeply hurt	Solitary, idle, incapable; "I am hopeless." "Leave me alone."
Obstacles to overcome	Doubt	Fear	Hatred; "I hate you."	Sense of having some deficiency; despair
Typical adult reactions	Annoyed by child's behavior	Anger	Feels hurt personally	Gives up; "It's hopeless."
Capacities to develop: what the child needs from the parent/adult	Creativity; building on strengths of what one does know to become able to experience success and build self-confidence	Courage and interest to face difficult situations; a process provided for learning how to access the support needed	Warmth and enthusiasm needed to heal the hurt; don't give up on the child; unconditional love	Having faith and hope in the child's ability to learn and succeed

Adapted from Balson (1988); Dinkmeyer (1989); and Steiner (1994)

The repetitive patterns live in our experiences in the body and we carry the traces and echoes of our lives within us. They can determine our behavior, responses, how well we connect with or are cut off from our inner resources, energy, relationships, wellbeing, creativity, purpose and depth of meaning in our life.[4] When we were in a

4 Ibid.

powerless position we instinctively coped and survived any perceived or real threats by developing defenses and strategies of protection. These defenses stay with us because they worked for us and only become a difficulty when we have a need to change or life presses us to change, to behave differently. Our interactions with our children as they grow and go through the different ages can activate all these layers. However, the most important thing to remember is that this is all about developing new capacities and the potential for this growth is hidden within these inner struggles. It is an opportunity presented by life to awaken and is presented to us in the guise of a personal "problem."

For this development to occur we need first to acknowledge that it is happening and to observe the activity in the sensation of the bodily experience, how we are triggered. This attention can begin to break the cycle of behaviors from repeating and protect our children from any destructive reactions. To understand these patterns, we can use the nonverbal languages of experience, which are: sensing bodily sensations, gesturing/movement of these sensations, visualization and sounds. These elements are the major tools of Psychophonetics counseling, and the combination of verbal and nonverbal ways of communicating become useful in developing the skills of inner communication, as the following example shows:

> A man is despairing to make a real connection to his nine-year-old son. He feels blocked and cut off from him, unavailable as the loving close father he wishes to be to him. It breaks his heart; it is not in his control. A nonverbal conversation evolves between the mature man and his inner child, the one who at nine years old was completely cut off from his father who was not there in his life and with the pain, hurt, anger and resentment still alive as they were then. The man finds a way to take care, to father his inner child. Soon after, his relationship to his son picks up, and they can start to relate to each other, closing the gap with love and warmth. The bridge is created inside first, then the bridging to the outside is made possible.[5]

5 Tagar (1996b:23).

Self-care

Simply placing a hand on a part of the body that is tense, on a part that has a contraction, a discomfort from some reaction during the daily interactions with others, can begin a way of being with experience as it is. These experiences resound in us and are usually located in a particular area of the body. Noticing the bodily sensation, becoming aware of the sensations and feelings, accepting it is there, not judging, denying, avoiding or trying to fix it, is doing something to begin the process of self-care. Listening to one's body is a starting point and an opportunity for making an inner connection. If we take a moment to do this for ourselves then a feeling, a memory, an insight or a story may emerge. From this starting point, and with a basic attitude of accepting the responsibility of self-care and self-parenting, one can acquire the tools to know more fully about one's inner experience, to encounter and change the inner dynamics, to take care of unresolved inner needs, hurts, and/or unexpressed speaking. Being present to ourselves in this way opens new potentials for self-knowledge, inner strength and warmth of heart to be present in our relationships.

There are many ways of developing and learning more about how we can support our children as a parent, as well as how we can take care through self-parenting. One process we can all do is learn to listen to the body; become aware of the presenting emotion or feeling; recognize this emotion/feeling as an opportunity for intimacy and learning; listen and validate this emotion/feeling; name the emotion/feeling; and explore options for finding the next step. This may mean just sitting with what is being experienced or talking to someone about how you are feeling, or it may mean seeing a counselor to explore and address deeper aspects, or there may be some other option that is relevant.

Creative Parenting

Parenting is a creative activity, and changing is inevitable as these inner disturbances are not necessarily problems if dealt with, but growing points of opportunities for us to take the next step in our development. Parenting is about learning on the job; the textbook is life itself. It inevitably means that we can learn from the child, that is, children can teach us to become parents. This means it is a process of trial and error, as parents are not made at birth but become parents over time. Love takes time. It is very much a journey of relationship, of "intimacy" (into-me-see).

The qualities of the child are needed for the resilience and hope toward creating more meaningful relationships in our lives. For instance, we may learn through mothering to strengthen with a stronger sense of selfhood, with inner strength to be more firm in the world. Fathering may teach us to soften, to express our feelings more, to develop nurturing qualities within and become a gentler person in the world. We all face the task of balancing the qualities of both gentleness and firmness in our lives, but it is very evident in the role of parenting and especially for single parents.

The opposite of learning from children is to deny their emotional experiences. For example, "it doesn't matter, children don't know what's going on." If we deny the validity of emotional experience in children, and in ourselves, we deny them the capacity to develop inner resources that support them in their development. These inner resources become hidden and have to develop in a different way and may be accessed later on in life when as adults, they seek help.

The unique contribution of Anthroposophy is that each human being is seen as a spiritual being, regardless of limitations or age, with the spirit of the child present as potential. As a parent or teacher we represent this spiritually perceived "I" of the child when we listen to the spirit within the child.[6] Based on the attitude that we are spiritual beings having a human experience, there are three principles regarding children that can guide us:

- Respect children by answering their questions until they are satisfied. This means being able to perceive how much a child can

6 Refer to Steiner's lecture 1 (Aug. 1924), in *Curative Education*.

take before moving on. In answering children's questions with respect, as much as we can, they learn that the question makes sense, that there is an answer to it, that they are taken seriously and that their thinking receives a response.

- Respect that children may want to do something that we don't want them to do and that they do not like it when we say "no"; or there are things they have to do that cannot be avoided, and they don't like it and scream. This means that I can tell children what to do but I cannot control how they feel, as they have a right to feel upset. For example, when the car seatbelt is put on a child, we cannot expect that he will be happy about it, so he may scream. Accepting that his crying is okay shows that the feeling life of the spiritual being in the child is respected.
- Respect children's will whenever possible even if they cannot explain it, for example, choosing a green or pink shirt. Listen to what is there, but not yet present within the child.

As adults, we represent their higher being and by allowing our capacities for Imagination, Inspiration, and Intuition to expand into this sphere, we can make choices based on knowing what is best for the child, or by listening to what the child is really trying to tell us. In light of this, we can learn to relate to children as if we are equal with a full being manifesting, and we can also listen to children and represent their developing "I."

Depression and Anxiety

It's helpful to mention the place of depression and anxiety as important tasks to be negotiated. We generally struggle to deny or overcome these emotions. We tend to want not to feel miserable and we want to avoid stressful situations. If however, we explore these emotions from a different perspective, we see they contain within them positive aspects that can contribute to our growth and development. For instance, depression or being reflective offers us the chance to slow down, to be in a more reflective mode, to have time to digest and integrate our experiences of what we have heard and learned.

Similarly, if our children or we are able to tolerate some anxiety and frustration, it enables our children to move from one stage of development to the next. For example, childhood illness is helpful as we learn about suffering, tolerance and perseverance, of stopping and taking care of needs. This brings us to the idea of tolerating some uncertainty and being able to allow our children to tolerate and stand some frustration at times. These experiences are important as preparation for the inevitable experiences of separation, loss and frustration that are part of life—if we learned as children to be angry and bewildered with our parents or leave our children that way, then there is very little preparation for developing inner resources.

Finally, to travel along the path of understanding the development of relationship—of the feeling heart, of emotional development and love—can be a fearful idea if painful memories are triggered. The process of containment of relationships between self, others and the world involves holding and balancing the interdependence of all these different levels of relationship. The image of the Russian doll is a useful way of holding these layers one within the other; from the outer world to inner self, layers of containment are: the community needs of family, family needs of father, father's needs of mother, and mother/baby needs. The family generally contains the family needs but also moves outward with its own layers needing support: of individual needs of family support, of family needs from others, and from the community. However, this isn't necessarily available for many separated and divorced parents, for people feeling more alone, alienated and unloved, hence the growing need for parent educators and counselors.

Educational and Therapeutic Supports

My work includes facilitating personal development groups as well as individual counseling and parenting sessions. The group process offers a space to encourage participants with practical ways of dealing with the issues that arise, to learn and develop new capacities and resources. The inner and interrelationship needs are addressed. Self-help skills are learned in a supportive and safe environment, with a listening space offered where participants can share their concerns and where creative forms of expression are explored. It is a creative, skills-oriented, therapeutic and educational group process based upon the participants' experiences and choices.

Individual counseling sessions allow clients to enter into the inner dynamics of their issues more deeply, using conversation, body awareness, sensing, gesture, visualization and sound therapy to understand how their experience is re-sounding in their body. The skills learned are designed specifically to suit each unique situation and experience. These nonverbal tools of body awareness can become self-help skills for use as needed in our daily life. The following poem expresses the therapeutic process of self-parenting and came in response to a request by a client to the counselor to summarize the process just experienced in a personal counseling session.

Motto of Self-parenting

My child was once in the hands of others
Adults who were my parents.
My child needed father and mother
As God in heaven promised me.
The adults around me did not qualify.
They were the best I could find.

Now I am an adult, too.
I might be better qualified for the job:
For the job of being, for my inner child
The father and the mother whom God had promised me

But between me as the loving adult
And me as the child in need
There are the traces of the unqualified adults
Who were my parents once.

They, incapable of the love and the protection
Which I was and I still am in need of,
They are present there now as traces of unsafety,
As traces of rejection and of fear.
These traces are mine now.
These things of darkness I must acknowledge as mine.

Then I can confront them, tell them off, dissolve them,
And put in their place the best of my adulthood:
My Inner Mother and my Inner Father,
The best of the universe in me.
With them I am now qualified
To care for my inner child

The people out there who were once my parents
I could then meet on equal terms.[7]

Conclusion

The hope and resilience we need for ourselves as adults involve taking care by listening to what is happening within the body, accepting and being with these soul experiences, as they offer an opportunity to know and choose options for further developing our resources and strengths. On this basis we can make a contribution to humanity by breaking old cycles of parenting and creating new forms of relationships not just with our own children but for future generations.

7 Tagar (1996b:24).

Chapter 7

Recovery and Healing from Grief and Loss of a Loved One

Rebecca Croad

How does Psychophonetics psychotherapy really help someone go through the process of grief of the loss of a loved one who has crossed the threshold of death? What is the client's experience of grief and loss? These questions interest me and so I have explored them further through counseling sessions with clients, through reading, and in writing this chapter.

Elizabeth Kübler-Ross talks about the stages of grief being denial, anger, bargaining, depression and, finally, acceptance.[1] She talks about these processes for the dying ones and for their caregivers before death, and they also apply to the caregivers post death as part of the process. Alan Wolfert, a writer and grief counselor, steps a little closer with six needs of mourning, which include acknowledging the reality of the death, embracing the pain of the loss, remembering the person who died, developing a new self-identity, searching for the meaning and receiving ongoing support from others.[2]

What tools are available to help embrace the pain of the loss? From my research in practice, clients were aware of their pain and suffering, however, they came with no idea of where they were in this process or how to work with it. It is a scary place that says, "Don't go there."

1 Kübler-Ross (1975).

2 Wolfert (1998:3–8).

What happens when one cannot access the cherished memories? Until the relationship with the loved one can be unraveled, a new self-identity may be hard to find.

Research shows that there is a natural psychological response, an orderly progress through distinct stages of bereavement.[3] They concluded that the focus on depression is misguided as it is *yearning* that dominates the psychological picture and a feeling that part of one is missing, that without that essential part, happiness is impossible.

Rudolf Steiner in his lecture on laughing and weeping has a beautiful description of the impoverished soul of a grief-stricken person:

> Suppose that for a long time we have loved someone who is not only closely related to our daily life, but also associated with particular soul experiences that arise from this close attachment. Suppose that this person is then torn from us for awhile. With that loss, a part of our soul experience is torn away; a bond between us and a being in the outer world is broken.... Something is torn from the "I," with the effect that the "I" passes into the astral body. In this case, since something is taken from the astral, it contracts—or more exactly, the "I" compresses the astral body.... The bodily expression of such a contraction is flowing tears. The astral body, having been left with gaps, as it were, wants to fill them by contracting, while making use of substances from its environment. In doing so, it also contracts the physical body and squeezes out the latter substances in the form of tears. What then, are these tears?... The tears are a sort of compensation for the stricken "I." The tears give the "I" a subconscious feeling of wellbeing as a certain balance is restored. People who cannot weep find sorrow and pain much harder to endure.[4]

What does this mean? I see tears as nature doing its work. The amount and duration of tears can be a monitor of how things are going with the client. In this chapter, I will focus on three female clients who attended counseling with grief and loss as their presenting issue. One

3 Maciejewski et al. (2007).

4 Steiner (2007).

client was still grieving one year after her loss, while the other two lost their fathers in the early years of their lives. The names of these women have been changed to protect their identities. I will give a brief description of each, highlighting key sessions, with a review and conclusions.

Natasha attended counseling over a period of two months. It has been a little under a year since a male friend committed suicide. Natasha has a lot of support and has tried various modalities to help with her grieving process. She is married with a seven-year-old son and is five months pregnant. Natasha had a long history with the deceased and since their teenage years they had an on-and-off sexual relationship, overriding current relationships at the time, including her present marriage.

In the beginning sessions, there is a lot of unraveling of herself in relation to the deceased person and her current partner. In the first session, her wish is to be able to be expressive and reconnect to her husband, rather than cringing from him. In this session she explores different layers of her beliefs. She feels her husband is trying to suffocate her spirit and there is a tendency to want to run away from this relationship and start again, which is a pattern in life regarding her personal relationships. Natasha creates an imaginary bridge to give a space for grieving in which it is safe to observe her present relationship and in which she is able to communicate across the bridge.

The second session is very important to Natasha's development in that she sees a father projection that she puts on her husband and what that does to her relationship with him. She discovers that her sexual being is very young and very intermingled with her deceased lover and is the cause of her wanting to have a continually exciting sexual life with no responsibilities in relationship, and of the codependency in which her "I am" presence has not fully arrived. Her wish in this session is to be able to step out of this cycle: "I want to find a place in me that is secure in me, with me." She wants to stop looking outward for the qualities of nurturer, protector, sexual being, and father.

In the third session, as she unravels herself from her partners, the pain still sits. She rationalizes her former lover's choice to take his life as tears fall and she describes how she has the need to fill every moment so she will not have to feel. She senses into the tiredness she is feeling and feels the weight of the continual sadness. I give her my empathic picture, of her inner self screaming in pain and hurt. She feels her heart immediately break and the pain does not go away, her wish is: "I wish to let go of the pain—to be lighter."

In my work as a therapist, embodied knowing, created in the in-between space between the client and myself, forms into a visualization of the Common Picture that helps me to understand how we may proceed into action from their wish. I am holding in my back space that this client is pregnant and that we have established drawing as her preferred medium for the action phase, as the physicality of gesture is too much for her. We enter through the experience happening now in the session—the suffering in the heart.

Natasha enters a process using drawings. The first drawing she calls "Broken." Natasha draws a red broken heart with a dagger in it, with black tears dripping from it. I place a second piece of paper below and ask her to continue drawing: She enters a vortex of blackness spiraling down to a dark cave with water before it. She enters the cave and draws it larger. She calls this drawing "Alone," which she expresses as the feeling every morning of not wanting to get out of bed, but hiding in her cave. She draws a mermaid harpooned on the shore, injured, bleeding and alone. When I ask her what she needs, she chooses to dissolve the harpoon and transform it into a pink flower, a flow of heart energy. She then explores the dagger in the opposite direction and draws a harpoon, with the former lover attached to the other end. She sees that she had chosen to be stuck here to deal with this stuff and then she draws a volcano erupting in anger, stating, "I want my power back." She then feels like a mermaid entering the flow of the water and knows she is not alone and can enter the flow of life again. Natasha later describes this session as lifting the black veil of grief from her face. She feels lighter, the darkness and heaviness have lifted, as well as the anxiety and pain. She no longer carries the fantasy of the former lover.

In the fourth and fifth sessions, Natasha works on owning her own energies. She grounds her inner strength and embraces her maturing, feminine, nurturing self. Natasha collects all that she needs to be more present, which was once replaced by her lover. She accesses a place of deep compassion that she embodies, not just conceptualizes. She discovers a sense of fullness she has never felt before. She was looking outside for a connected man so she could feel more connected, and this is what she had felt with her former lover. She has accomplished her second wish, "to find a safe place in me, with me." It is work in progress, as the untwining of her being with her former lover has to occur, and then the owning of her own self has to develop before she can find her safe, connected self.

Rowan is a thirteen-year-old female. Her father died when she was seven years old, her brother was nine, and her younger sister was four. She had undertaken six to seven sessions with a counselor in the previous year while living in Queensland. She is suffering bouts of mild depression and is being monitored by her doctor. Rowan's main reason for coming to counseling was about her mood swings, due to feelings of grief and loss. With her father's death, her mother became depressed and Rowan became the physical and emotional rock for them. She lost her father, her mother and her youth. She now has no passion, no playfulness and feels old beyond her years. Rowan is very angry a lot of the time. Her wish is, "to be able to remember the fun times with dad, not what I miss about him."

She feels stuck in what is missing in her life, since now this is all she can see in the future. It is paralyzing her from being functional in her present life. Her soul feels impoverished and I can see her life body contracting. Rowan wants to feel expanded when she thinks of her father. What gets in the way? The example from life is every day she wakes up angry with, "I want to go and say, 'Hi dad.'" In the action phase of the session, she discovers on waking that her heart is dark, blocked and sad, then it explodes—she feels sick, angry and hurt—and following this, her heart slowly shrivels. These all appear to be reactions, so I suggest she focus on a moment before she was so conscious in her waking moment.

She finds a moment in waking when she is glad to be alive, but as her father died in his sleep, she fears going to sleep. In gesturing this experience, she discovers herself all knotted in fear. She is tired of being knotted. She sees herself at seven (her age at father's death) with her heart pumping too fast; she is scared; she has lost her protector. She enters a vulnerable pit where it is dark, cold, lonely and wet. She is drowning in her own sorrow. She pictures herself in a graveyard, scared and looking for someone to pull her out. Rowan invokes the qualities of safety and strength remembered from her father, yellow in color and the size of the earth. She invokes and connects with the feeling of the father as her imagined inner quality of protection. She spends a long time in this position, enjoying being in the feeling of protection. Rowan tells me later that this session changed the way she woke up, enabling her to embrace the more comforting memories rather than waking in fear and anger.

In the second session, after a conversation Rowan makes a wish: "to be able to express the confusion, hurt and upset." In the action phase, she senses into the confusion she has experienced since her father's death, and names it "unexpressed feelings." It is a place of blackness with no guiding light to the end of the tunnel. Rowan is stuck in this darkness and something is stopping her from being happy. She enters an enter–exit–behold process and finds herself feeling suffocated in water, trapped there by firm plastic. On a second entry into this, she finds her soul split in two; her father has taken half her soul with him. Staying with the wish, I ask Rowan to express all that was unsaid and felt for the past seven years onto the pillow, and she uses the sound "Grrr" to enhance her expression. The plastic ripped right across the oceans and she finds herself sitting in the light on a sandy beach, happy. She sits in connection with her father in relation to the split soul and feels complete with his love and guidance nourishing her soul.

In a subsequent session, Rowan reports she has a new perspective of her father's loss, and no longer feels stuck. She has a renewed sense of feeling fresher and there is more happiness in her daily life. Rowan had been stuck in a pit of sorrow and the longer time went on, with more memories to add, the well just got deeper and deeper, with a sense of a drowning element for Rowan. She shows me the power of expressing sorrow, which had a releasing effect on the astral and the etheric bodies, by expressing the emotional and bringing a renewed sense of life to the etheric body.

The client's drawings done during the sessions are similar to those of another person called Marilyn, a fifty-three-year-old woman who was grieving the loss of her partner and marriage due to her husband's recent mental illness. Marilyn describes her heart is "full of grief, with no joy, laughter or fun. It was all dark, verbal anger, rage, screaming, shouting, pain in heart, alone in my grief." As she progressed through her process, Marilyn could experience and draw a yellow heart nurtured with love, gentleness and compassion, her heart opened, free of its confinement, finding joy and lightness.[5] This seems to confirm that patterns of grief can be of a similar nature, with the flow into life freeing the heart as a resource of love and compassion and a sense of lightness.

Sophie lost her father when she was only nine, and is now thirty-three years of age, married with three young children. At twenty-one, Sophie recalls having grief counseling for anger issues. Her main issue around her father's death is the way she and her sister were treated at the time, excluded from it all and the relationship with her mother since. Sophie had a very loving relationship with her father but not with her mother. After his death, her mother was unavailable and the girls were left at their neighbor's house. In the first session, Sophie deals with self-worth and asking for what she needs, without feeling unworthy and making a big story out of nothing. This related to her relationship to her mother in the hard years following her father's death, with a tendency to disappear and hide as a coping mechanism.

5 Steele (2005). See chapter 3: "Marilyn: The Way of the Heart."

In this session, Sophie learns how to invoke the qualities of the inner mother she needs now.

In the second session, Sophie is overwhelmed and exhausted by her daughter's constant clinging demands. She is very teary and feels lost as to what to do, talking a lot about finding outer resources to help her daughter. Her first wish is about her daughter, "for her to be a happy, confident, secure little girl." Instantly the tears flow, as in saying this she recognizes that she wishes this for herself as well. Sophie recognizes this link and her second wish is "to have knowledge and strength." She is seeking a renewed source to help her stay strong and coping for her daughter and family. This session is very relevant as Sophie is very tired of parenting—as she parented her own mother since the death of her father. In the action phase, Sophie learns to let go and receive what she really needs by invoking the inner caring mother. This new knowledge for Sophie is her strength, as she understands the importance of nurturing her inner self so she has the strength to stand by her daughter.

In the third session, Sophie recognizes that she did not trust her mother from a very early age. Her dad was her lifeline and connection to warmth and love. Since then, she often felt disconnected from other people in her life. Sophie's wish is "to feel connected and supported." Sophie wants to explore the experience of not feeling connected and enters bodily in sensing and gesture into the example of always feeling disconnected in the face of others. This experience transforms her to age nine and the day her father died; even though it happened twenty-four years ago, it still lives in her. Sophie has always had a memory of wanting to crawl under the table to get away from the rest of the family, but what she really wants is to have a warm soft mother to soothe her breaking heart. In this process she connects to the feeling of nurturing a broken heart.

As she draws her broken heart and sees herself alone in grief with her head down in darkness, she says with surprise, "I have stayed like this ever since," hence, the feeling of disconnection from people in her life since. She then draws the warm-hearted nurturer and experiences receiving this nurturing quality using movement and sound. She draws what it does to her heart until she feels complete and radiant. As she allows herself to reconnect to her father, she remembers how it felt to have his loving arms around her, and as she also feels the missing of the last twenty-four years, many tears were shed. Sophie allows herself to receive the qualities of softness, warmth, kindness, safety and understanding remembered from her father. She wishes she had received this connection when she was growing up, but she now feels whole. In relation to the wish, she is now connected to the warmth and softness of the mother nurturer and the father she lost. Sophie has a new connection and vibrancy in her heart.

Summary Comments

For Sophie the loss of her dad and the disliking of her mother created an identity crisis for her through her growing-up years. Her self-esteem suffered under her mother's negativity. For Sophie, the aftermath of her father's death has been that of loneliness, with a distinct lack of love and warmth, and loss of connection to her heart. Both she and Rowan, being oldest daughters, took on mothering at a young age, both suffering as a consequence.

In the cases of loss of a loved one experienced by young children, as in Rowan's case, there can be a partial split of the soul. This also was experienced by another client sitting at the bedside alone when her father died in her presence. She experienced and remembered this again, in a Psychophonetics session with Robin Steele, as a leaving of the ten-year-old child/soul going with the father as he died, and being in the spiritual world, not wanting to return but having to say goodbye and continue living. When children are so bonded and dependant upon a parent, they may wish to leave with them. To discover that moment of their consciousness leaving can enlighten present-day behavior and the choice to return is empowering, enabling one to be more consciously present in body and soul in present-day life.

The main process for grief and loss of a loved one included becoming more conscious, being in their power, and in every case was followed up by connecting with inner and outer resources. The life body of the grieving person becomes contracted into something heavy, dark and all-encompassing, leaving the person feeling disempowered and not able to live fully. In grief, people can become stuck. When we see the image of a heart speared and broken, shedding black tears and shattered in half, could this be our own doing? Do we do that to our own hearts? Could children do this to their own hearts? Or, is it the impact of how we experience something done to us? In my clinical experience, loss can be experienced as an injury, with our soul and life forces contracting in response to the missing. I believe there is a place we can go to be resuscitated and healed with new life forces. It is not a place clients are aware of through conversation, but through body awareness, gesture, visualization, sound work and drawing, the client can discover deeper places within.

Does time heal grief? I don't know that it does fully. From clinical research, my observation is that grief lives through time. If we were taught as the Buddhists believe, to keep our hearts open and allow all that comes in the loss, and give ourselves time to honor all, then maybe grieving would be a process different from what most of us experience in life. Generally, we are not a society that welcomes grief; we know very little about the resources to help us through such times or allow ourselves time to heal in our busy society. We rather use busyness to keep us from feeling pain. Pain as demonstrated in the case studies is the open wound of the heart and the contraction of the soul to protect the hurt. This makes sense as the loss of a loved one is an affair of the heart.

To begin the journey of recovery, clients may need firstly to address long-term unresolved issues that may be mixed in with the relationship to their loved one. It may be un-entwining of the souls of a lover or partner, or the exhaustion of parenting from a young age due to the unavailable surviving parent. Or, it may be addressing issues of an existing relationship, as shown in Natasha's case with her husband, and in Sophie's case with her mother and family. In both cases, they all connected to the loss of the loved one.

Common Processes and Themes

The following common themes are gathered from my experience of working through grief using Psychophonetics and drawing.

- *We can enter through sensing the bodily contraction or the wound.* By traveling into the blackness and loneliness to join the darkness of the surviving one—or rather the barely surviving one who has been frozen in time—and to feel fully the pain and loneliness. This one knows something and can discover what was missing at the time?
- *Invoking the missing quality of what was needed at the time*—For the adult loss, as with Natasha's case, it was simply love. For the child's loss, as in Rowan and Sophie's case, it was the warmth and love of their lost parent, the presence of an available surviving parent, and the safe space to be able to express their grief and loss.
- *Connecting to the missing quality within oneself and invoking through imagination and receiving the missing quality, allows a healing process to take place and allows a space for feeling*—Often, receiving the missing quality will reveal how impoverished the soul has been. In a counseling session, people are encouraged to feel the missing in the depths of their soul, which allows the healing process to work because, while they are reexperiencing the missing, there is also a receiving that can be invoked to fill the soul with love and light. This can bring a new sense of warmth and vibrancy and new expressions of heart and soul.
- *Drawing, moving and sounding the new life forces encourages deep healing.*
- *Once people gain an inner resource, they can reconnect spiritually with their loved one*—This can enhance the healing and connection of the relationship or, in Natasha's case, gave

her the impetus to motivate her anger and will to take her power back.

Useful Recommendations

- Give a space to feel and to breathe, as sometimes a moment of quietness in a safe environment is exactly what a person needs.
- In my work with clients, the entry point for working through grief and loss seems to be mostly through the heart, though the direction of the client's wish must always be the guiding direction.
- If the counselor is aware that the client is dealing with grief and loss, some enlivening activity at the beginning of the action phase of the session can be useful to encourage being present in the body, for sensing and feeling. As grief is in the body, it is not a cognitive process; it has to be felt.
- At the end of a session, practitioners may need to check/sense their own body, to clear and restore their own energy. This would be especially significant if grief and loss is your main career choice, such as in palliative care.

Conclusion

Psychophonetics counseling/psychotherapy can be helpful in the recovery and healing process of grief from the loss of a loved one who has crossed the threshold of death, especially when using body sensation, gesture, visualization, creating a space for feeling and drawing, the invisible can become visible. Visibility is knowledge and new consciousness is powerful, because then we can see how it is, do something about it, and bring in more "I am" presence. I want to firstly acknowledge the beauty of the process of deep empathic responses in understanding grief, for if we go there we can then understand the darkness, pain and loneliness our clients may be experiencing, and be able to provide the safety for them to be open and express their feelings. For many of my clients, they had no idea that they were living with hurt in their heart;

they were experiencing pain and suffering with no understanding of why it would not go away. Once visible, clients are able, with the tools of Psychophonetics, to provide for themselves their own remedy for resuscitation of their life forces. This enables them to reenter the flow of life out of the black veil of grief and to be able to gain a new connection and relationship to their loved one. This new knowledge and the ability to be able to visualize and connect to their loved ones can be taken home and used as a future rescue remedy if needed; they are not dependant on the counselor. If relevant, a ritual of saying goodbye can also be created in the final stages of the process, done with others or alone, either in the therapy session or somewhere else that is meaningful for this person.

We can see that if our heart is hurting, then we are not fully present in the now and the future. When we know the depths of our sorrow, then joy, laughter, love and happiness become more meaningful. Our heart is essential for joy and engaging with others, especially those we love. Grief and loss teach us the importance of our heart, that life is precious and our loved ones are a gift.

Editor's Comment

When a loved one passes over the threshold of death, the potential gift is that we can come to know that love does not die by learning to build our soul and spirit connections with the departed soul. The following verse by Rudolf Steiner can give us comfort and inspiration to develop these connections.

> No boundaries separate
> Where spirit links sustain
> Light-brilliant,
> Love-radiant
> Eternal soul bonds.
>
> So I am in your thoughts,
> So you in mine.

I was united with you,
Remain united within me.

We will converse
In the language of eternal being.
We will be active
Where deeds take effect,
We will weave in Spirit
Where human thoughts are woven
In the Word of eternal Thoughts.[6]

---

6 R. Steiner, *Mantrische Sprüche. Seelenübungen II. 1903–1925* (GA 268); not available in English.

Chapter 8

Forgetting and Remembering: A Path of Initiation

Judy Emma Greenberg

Where do memories live, the memories of traumatic events that we have "forgotten"? Do we ever really forget these experiences that shape our lives and define who we think we are, out of both their reality and our perception of that reality?

If this lifetime and its circumstances are a part of a larger destiny relating to my past and evolution as an individual into that destiny, the nature of what I experienced in my childhood and its impact has a meaning completely different from the one I initially ascribed to it. "What we experience as destiny in one lifetime is related to our actions in previous earthly lives,"[1] and it is in this context that I used Anthroposophy as a guide, to embark on my conscious journey of inquiry.

My father died when I was four years old, and soon after that I was sexually abused. I then "forgot" this experience and I "forgot" who I really am, in my spiritual essence. This is a journey of discovering self, who I really am, out of the maze of darkness, secrets, delusions, identities, and stories created to make sense of and to survive well in my life. One day, when I was thirty-eight years old, I remembered an experience I was able to confirm, which encouraged me to trust subsequent memories.

1 Steiner (1994b:85).

Whereas the focus in this chapter is forgetting, in terms of its subsequent impact, it is predominately about childhood sexual abuse. There is also an overlap of issues arising out of this relating to the death and loss of my father and the aggressive, threatening behavior by another man who was present in my childhood and who, for the purpose of this chapter, I will call Chip. The transformation of these experiences is really my transformation as a human being.

Forgetting, in the way I forgot, is generally known as a defense mechanism called repression. It is well documented that Freud considered forgetting of this nature to be an involuntary repression of thoughts or traumatic events into the unconscious. Another psychological definition says that, "these memories don't just disappear; they continue to influence our behavior. For example, a person who has repressed memories of abuse suffered as a child may later have difficulty forming relationships."[2]

The individual forgets because remembering is too painful. For young children in particular, traumatic experiences are too frightening to remember and, for most, are beyond their capacity to integrate. After remembering came denial that it could have happened. I naively believed it did not have a big impact on me, but I felt a sense of shame and kept this new knowledge a secret for a long time. As I revisited the memories still in my body[3] after all these years, I came to understand that I was just not ready to remember. I came to appreciate the wisdom of a body–mind that enables forgetting.

"Sexual abuse includes any sexual act or experience which is forced upon a person, or which occurs as a result of coercion."[4] It usually occurs for the gratification of the older individual and includes rape, incest, inappropriate touching, verbal or physical taunting

2 Accessed from the internet: www.psychology.about.com/od/dindex/Psychology_Glossary_D_Index.htm.

3 Body for this author refers to Steiner's model of the human being with "Body" as being comprised of a physical body, life/etheric body, an astral/soul body and the "I."

4 Alic (2001: para.1).

or harassment, exposure to pornographic material and is often accompanied by threats or bribes, and sometimes, violence. Secrecy is also a common feature. The definition of sexual abuse varies amongst cultures, and over time.[5]

"Many victims report that they mentally leave their bodies, to dissociate themselves from the physical event."[6] This adds another dimension to forgetting, as you cannot remember if you are not there. Leaving the body is a real experience for many people: "who have survived sexual abuse under the age of seven"[7] and that was my experience. I understand it as being a way of surviving the experience, of it happening to the body and not the self. My experience of the return of memories is that I did not remember until I was present enough in my body, which was holding the memories. This was well into my healing journey. A significant part of therapy is supporting people to stay present in their bodies and to observe and to understand their own bodily sensations.[8]

Being present in my body more fully was often a battle, sometimes my body hurt all over, often just in specific places.[9] I was reluctant to feel the pain and the old pattern to leave was strong, but I kept choosing "to stay." Rudolf Steiner describes how "profoundly disturbing mental images can be when they cannot be summoned from the soul's depths into consciousness, but instead continue to swim along with the etheric current in those unconscious depths of the soul life. They then generate all their strength into the physical body." [10] Being more fully in the body is a crucial element of healing. Making "friends" with one's body, the vehicle of the abuse often hated by people who have experienced sexual

5 Alic (2001).

6 Alic (2001:para.7).

7 Tagar (2001:11).

8 This is confirmed by Rothschild (2000:3).

9 I was later diagnosed with having fibromyalgia and arthritis. I know that there is a connection between the pain of these and the emotions from the past held in the body. Getting present to the pain usually leads to an emotional release and instant pain relief.

10 Steiner (1999:149).

abuse, is a necessary step for further healing. Once the painful memories in the body are reexperienced in this supportive way, it is possible to reconnect to the body in a healthy and joyful way.

Even if we can remember, the trauma of such an incident can render us unable to feel the pain of it, and as such, we forget the pain, and this delays the healing process. From my experience, the memory alone is not enough for healing, but remembering by reexperiencing the feelings and emotions is necessary. After I became aware of the sexual abuse, I was able to talk about it, but at that time, could not feel anything. I did not know I was disconnected from feeling until I began feeling again. The intense emotions made me realize that I had not been ready to feel pain or anger, because it hurt so much or scared me.

Initially, remembering occurred in a number of ways: when I was ill with chronic fatigue syndrome (CFS), between sleeping and fully awakening, when being aware of pain or sensation in my body, during meditation or breathing practice, in counseling sessions, in life, during conversations with others, or just when triggered by someone or an event. It also occurred during yoga classes and bodywork sessions, such as massage or chiropractic care.[11] A common link was when I was in a state of being present and focused or very still or both. The memories arose irregularly, sometimes months or even years apart. They occurred as flashbacks, pictures of scenes, thoughts, feelings and sometimes with bodily sensations and pain. I trusted them as the initial picture memory was confirmed by my mother; a childhood event that, until the moment of remembering, I had forgotten. My earliest remembering was not about the sexual abuse; that came later. This first picture memory was of a scene in the kitchen of my family home in which, as a seven year old, I was sitting with my five-year-old brother, with Chip in front of us and my mother standing to the side against the kitchen sink. Chip was being a bully, yelling at us and demanding an

11 According to Rothschild (2000:37) information is transmitted between the brain and all points in the body through the nervous system. Somatic memory relies on this communications network.

answer to a question. Not only did I remember the experience and all the fear that was part of it, but I was back there as the little girl that I was then.[12] I reexperienced the thoughts and the terror from that time, moment by moment. I revisited this scene many times later, reconnecting to the anger and betrayal I felt toward my mother for not protecting me. The emotions experienced at seven years old were internalized and then arose thirty-one years later when the memory returned, and healing could begin. Safety is an important component in remembering. Immediately after Chip's death, memories came flooding in from my childhood—it was now safe enough to remember.

Forgetting sexual abuse or any other trauma also relates to the way it is handled at the time of its occurrence and with its subsequent impact. If a child discloses what happened and the response is one of acceptance and appropriate action, healing can begin.[13] However, if no one noticed or responded appropriately, the damage is compounded.

Secrecy plays a pivotal role in the delaying of the healing process. Shame about what happened and fear of the consequences of telling keeps children silent, as does the threat by the perpetrator of harming the child or loved one if anything is spoken. In the case of the latter, a number of behaviors, symptoms, and disorders may develop in order to cope and ultimately avoid the pain of remembering the abuse. It is a common occurrence for early-childhood sexual abuse to be forgotten, understandable given the trauma associated with it. All sexual abuse, and certainly child sexual abuse, is damaging. The trauma continues long after the abuse stops until healing begins, even if that is not until many years later. The experience of the self is imprinted in early childhood and a healthy self-concept is based on this experience.[14]

12 This is confirmed by Bass (1997:74-75) who says that because memories are stored in our bodies, it is possible to reexperience the emotions of the original abuse.

13 Bass and Davis (1997:34).

14 Glöckler (2000:12).

The lack of opportunity or choice to begin a healing process gives rise to the potential of multiple issues. When the healing process does not begin immediately, or soon after an abuse, the memories, feelings and associated emotions, the beliefs about oneself and the perpetrator in relation to the experience, don't just disappear. They do not go away just because the awareness is not on them or we have forgotten them. They have an impact on all aspects of life—on one's ability to trust, feel safe, have healthy intimate relationships, and on parenting and on one's work. Ultimately, if not addressed, they have the potential to manifest as bodily symptoms. Steiner makes this point: "Below the surface of consciousness, many mental images are active that can cause illness."[15]

What manifests in the body is both understood and described in different ways. It is through illness, often in adulthood, that severe trauma from childhood is remembered.[16] This resonates with my own experience of being diagnosed with chronic fatigue syndrome and at the same time remembering traumatic events from my childhood. I understand this as being a return of that which was repressed. My illness had taken me out of the busyness of my life. I became still enough to be able to hear my inner voice. My body became a source of all I had forgotten. My first remembering occurred on waking one morning feeling heavy and sad. I said to my then-husband, "I feel like I have just lost my father." My father had actually died when I was four years old. For a while after that, I went through a grieving process and "remembered" the pain and sadness of losing him.

Psychophonetics regards the body as an absorber, carrier, reflector, communicator, and transformer of experience and as a map for the landscape of our experience.[17] The memories of childhood sexual abuse are often not easily accessed, but are there regardless. This can take a long time and in some cases, it may not happen at all, leaving the person suffering at the hands of something seemingly without a reason.

15 Steiner (1999:149).

16 Glöckler (2000:14).

17 Tagar (1993:94-97).

From a psychotherapeutic perspective, people experiencing bodily symptoms are often unaware of any underlying anxiety. This was also my experience, including an eating disorder/sugar addiction, illness and numerous other more subtle symptoms. These were seemingly too extreme to relate only to the death of my father and with no other obvious reason, until I remembered the sexual abuse. At age forty–five I had a memory of being sexually abused at nine years old, and at age forty-nine a memory of sexual abuse at age four. I had no awareness of either event previously and after the memory of the first event came, no awareness of the second for four years.

Once the memories of abuse arose, I began to read about the impact of sexual abuse and to understand the source and depth of the issues I faced. This led to more conscious, deeper work. For awhile, I did not tell anyone about remembering. I had kept it a secret, even from myself for so long that I needed time to integrate. I started by telling the health professionals that I was seeing. Telling others was challenging, and I chose carefully who to share with. The issue of being believed, or not, and the question of false memories kept holding me back. Also, there was often an issue of pain and sensitivity to the response of others, as well as their ability to be accepting and empathic in the face of this revelation.

The return of memories and issues arose organically, and for a while, I worked with them by myself. Eventually, I needed therapeutic support, which Tagar confirms is a beneficial way of dealing with these issues: "Survival from past sexual abuse is for most people an uphill lonely battle, because of the incompatibility between their adult consciousness and the nature of the consciousness of the younger person they were when the traumatic imprints of the abuse experience took place."[18]

My journey with therapists and my own experiences took me through a psychotherapeutic process of learning about repressed memories, feelings and emotions relating to my father's death, and verbal/emotional abuse by Chip. I learned about the connection between these, the fatigue and pain in my body, why and how I learned to not feel and

---

18 Tagar (2001:15).

not be in my body. Also, I learned about the range of emotions such as fear, anger, grief, which I used to avoid feeling and why I used sugar, avoided conflict, reacted to particular men and to particular situations, didn't trust, felt shame, self-hatred, guilt, and self-doubt. I learned about why I regularly fainted and why a fibroid tumor grew. I believe that CFS and the growth of the fibroid were manifestations of what I could not let myself remember.

Once I became aware of the sexual abuse, I had a new reference point. I visited the issues more than once, each time accessing a deeper layer, but with no logical order to what I felt needed addressing at any particular time.

> The nature of the retrieval of traumatic memory is that it comes in bits and pieces, permeates through to the conscious mind and feelings as it is ready. It seemed to have a life all of its own. I have flashes of pictures, of thoughts, "a child's voice" how could he do that to me, tears, anger, and in between, life goes on. There is still a level of disbelief. (personal journal, August 1998)

Before I remembered, there had always been the sense of an underlying problem. I felt disconnected from my sexual essence and my sexual energy. I now understand that until I was ready to remember, it necessitated that I remain shut down to that energy, disinterested in sexual intimacy with strong reactions of fear when I experienced men's attraction to me or when seeking sexual intimacy. Also, during the healing from chronic fatigue, a number of health practitioners asked me if I had been sexually abused, but at the time I did not relate to this concept at all.

The first indication of this possibility arose in June 1997. A fellow student in the Psychophonetics counseling course spoke to me about some childhood sexual interference she had experienced, and I had a very strong reaction to her story. This was during a training weekend and a staff member took me into a quiet room to support me. I was asked to be fully present to what was going on for me. The following description comes from my journal:

> Soon after, I began to feel emotional, distracted, and coughing a lot. I started to cry, sob and heave and then lost touch with present reality. I relived something awful. I dropped to the floor, curled up in a ball, holding my stomach, crying and screaming and feeling as though I had been punched. My breathing was restricted. I was seven years old... When I came out of this experience I had a memory of a day at the circus with a cousin of my mother and her husband whom I called aunty and uncle. They wanted me to smile for a photograph and for whatever reason I felt very strongly, and can still feel that feeling of not wanting to smile; even telling my brother not to smile. What does all this mean—that my friend's speaking evoked this response in me and that I had that memory. (personal journal, June 9, 1997)

This was one of my first experiences of the profound nature of Psychophonetics counseling/psychotherapy. The sequence of remembering the sexual abuse unfolded gradually in the following way. In July 1998, I had a strong sense that I had been sexually interfered with, and in August 1998, I had a clear picture of an incident at age nine, however, I didn't know who the abuser was. In 2001, I remembered being sexually interfered with when I was four years old. In 2002, Chip died and memories started flooding in. I knew then that there had been two different abusers: Chip when I was nine years old and an "uncle," when I was four years old.

These experiences show a strong connection between body/mind, feelings and emotions, on one hand, and innate wisdom, on the other. The body is a messenger of what was forgotten, a vehicle for guidance toward healing from my "higher self," in which I trusted more and more. I had a growing interest in spiritual ideas as I began to experience this inner guidance and a growing commitment to being more embodied.

I met Anthroposophy and Psychophonetics counseling when I was forty-five, seven years after the first "remembering." Meeting Anthroposophy was life changing and provided an answer to my question about why remembering started when it did. Anthroposophy also made sense of my experiences in a way that nothing prior had. I discovered a body of knowledge and a way of being that supported my often-tumultuous journey, a path of knowing, of self-knowledge, a spiritual path. The anthroposophic model of the human being[19] resonates in me and the spiritual worldview encapsulated in Anthroposophy inspires the possibility of healing and transformation. Through doing practices that encouraged spiritual development, such as contemplation, meditation, and a breathing practice, I went within more deeply.

Psychophonetics counseling is an integral part of my journey, firstly as a client, then as a student, and later as a practitioner. This approach welcomes and enables remembering through the use of the body as a source of knowing. It also includes practices to support healing and development that can be used at home, thus encouraging self-management. I learned a number of things: to take responsibility in a new way, how to create inner safety, about my defense patterns, about self-care on all levels, how to access and strengthen my inner resources, and how to speak rather than reacting or silencing myself. I learned that I had a younger wounded self and how to care for her/myself, and how to be more compassionate toward her/myself. I learned about empathy, how to connect to feelings, how to release anger in a healthy way, how to create a healthy personal space, how to recognize and work with reactions and projections, how to strengthen the will, how to gain mastery over my lower self, how to stop being hard on myself, and how to stop resisting what is. I started to make good choices more often. The research and specific tools in Psychophonetics counseling for recovery from past sexual abuse provide a unique opportunity for healing on a deeper and more profound level. Now, as a practitioner of Psychophonetics, I have worked with many people and am often in awe at the depth of what is possible for clients to explore, uncover, heal and transform.

As healing progressed, I noticed that transformation was taking place in many ways of being and areas of my life. In particular, the

19 The anthroposophic model of a human being as body, soul and spirit.

healing and transformation of my relationship to my sexual essence and energy and of my ability to be sexually intimate has been a slow process, understandably. It has also been a challenging and fulfilling journey that continues, but writing about it is another chapter in another book.

An integral component of healing and transformation is taking responsibility for one's own healing. This means learning to trust our inner knowing and taking the necessary steps, both in seeking out health professionals and having a discipline for self-care. Surrender is also an essential component of true healing and transformation. On one level, it is about learning to trust others and on another, it is about having the courage to let go of trying to understand and control everything, having the humility to pray and ask for help, and the faith to trust in a higher source or spirit.

Forgiving is another essential component of the healing and transformation process. Embracing forgiveness and choosing to forgive are important elements. Remembering brought me awareness of what happened, as well as pain, anger and blame. To truly forgive I needed to experience and let this all go, and to forgive myself for the blame that was turned inward. Surrendering to something bigger than myself and my circumstances enabled that forgiveness and I realized that in some situations there was nothing to forgive, just acceptance of what is.

One significant turning point in the healing journey was the moment I realized that much suffering occurred from the stories I told myself in relation to the abuse and what I made it mean. For example, I told myself: "I am evil, dirty, deserve to be punished, and unworthy of good." It was liberating to realize these self-judgments were not true, but were stories I told myself, and possibly were told to me by the abusers. Another was the realization that, even though on one level I was a victim of the abuse, on another, more spiritual, level, I was not. This is not something I will explain in this chapter, but it is a knowing that comes from meditation practices, as insights that resonate as true. Knowing this helped me to move beyond living life as a victim, being powerless, blaming and angry.

Remembering takes us beyond our childhood experiences and suffering. Transformation of experience is really our transformation as a human being. I have an ever-growing sense of self (higher self), the "I," or spiritual essence. By retrieving many aspects of the self that were stuck in past, unintegrated experiences, there is now more of me present in the remembering of who I am. I experience who I am differently now—as being more peaceful, present, joyful, loving, grateful, wise, courageous, trusting, aware, self-reflective, empowered. I live more authentically, noticing more beauty and goodness in people and the world. I am also more aware of the pain and suffering, as well as our resilience as human beings, and the strength of the human spirit.

I am remembering that I am more than the identities that I took on, the duality of my personality, my mask, my darkness. I am remembering who I am: a human being physical/spiritual, a member of both worlds. Forgetting this is the human condition, remembering it transforms. I am also remembering events, thoughts, feelings, often with pictures, knowledge, people and places, not from this life, yet known intimately. I am remembering that I have been here before.[20] Reading about the experiences of others has supported the acceptance of my own experiences. For me these experiences connect to the idea of initiation and of remembering as a path of initiation.

Remembering, healing and transformation of past experiences has been a personal path of initiation into the mysteries of life, being human as physical/spiritual beings, the spiritual world, consciousness, remembering, the past, other lifetimes, karma, destiny, our purpose here, our ability to develop higher faculties, and working with spirit, heart/love. These experiences are in other realms of consciousness, accessible during moments of stillness and focus, and are part of my journey. At these times, I am most connected to spirit and occasionally see or hear the presence of the spiritual world and know that I am being supported

20 Steiner (1962:30) states: "the human being goes from one incarnation to another...has passed through repeated earth lives."

and guided. In remembering specific scenes, thoughts and feelings from other lifetimes, there is often a link between the past and what is found in present issues, mostly in the inner dynamics.[21]

The expansion of consciousness and the mysteries of the heart and of love are at the core of life itself and the journey of every human being. With the early loss of love due to my father's death and with what followed, my heart became very defended and closed, particularly in certain circumstances, as this was safer than risking more pain. During the journey of remembering, my heart gradually opened as I allowed myself to feel the pain and heal. I now experience love more fully and have found a place of peace within me. In that place my heart is open to fulfilling something within that wants to reach out to others to encourage them to find this place in themselves, as a way to help create a peaceful world. I think of this as my higher purpose in life, maybe my destiny.

We do not ever really forget the memories of traumatic events, or any events, as they live on somewhere within. The opportunity to access them is available to us when the time is right, and the remembering is the potential for our development. This path of initiation is through choosing to heal and transform experiences from early childhood that were forgotten, then remembered. It has been and continues to be a profound and powerful journey.

21 Lachman (2003:93) speaks about a kind of consciousness called *hypnagogia* as a state that can be "telepathic; precognitive; and it can reach back in time."

Chapter 9

Healing Past Childhood Sexual Abuse: Common Themes

Yehuda Tagar and Robin Steele

The number of people who suffer from past and present sexual abuse far exceed the numbers affected by cancer or heart disease. The long-term consequences of being abused sexually cover a wide range of symptoms such as low self-esteem, fear and anxiety, depression and psychiatric illness, with a vulnerability to substance abuse, destructive relationships, repetition of abuse, and inappropriate sexual behavior. The cost for the individual and society as a whole is high. Whereas a physical attack affects the physical body, an emotional attack affects the soul life, and neglect of people affects their life body, sexual abuse attacks the human spirit. This is what makes this experience so severe.

This chapter highlights some themes emerging from clinical experience and case study research, in Australia and South Africa, of adults' recovery and healing from past childhood sexual abuse. Encouraging people to articulate nonverbally the reality of their experience held in the bodily memory allows them to express creatively what they cannot express so easily in words. The nonverbal language of sensing, gesture, visualization and sound work gives a language with which to access the experience of these patterns, as it goes beyond any differences in language and culture. From many years of clinical observation and the phenomenological exploration of clients' experiences from case studies, the following themes or clusters of experience were found to be crucial for empathy and effective inner work with this issue.

Main Clusters of Experiences

The following clusters of experience[1] also include drawings and descriptions by Jess,[2] who attended a number of Psychophonetics counseling sessions in 2001. At that time, Jess was twenty-three years old and had suffered digestive problems from age thirteen, which became worse throughout her teenage years, and she was diagnosed as having Irritable Bowel Syndrome at age seventeen and chronic fatigue syndrome (CFS) at eighteen, which lasted for about five years. She had seen doctors, naturopaths, Chinese herbalists, homeopaths and traditional chiropractors throughout this period with little result. At age twenty she began seeing a kinesiologist, and for the first time became aware of herself as being more than just a physical body. This started an inner journey to seek a deeper connection with herself. At twenty-two years old, Jess saw a Network Chiropractor, and at twenty-three years, she was experiencing a general "stuck-ness" in life and a new emotion of anger. She says, "I don't know where it's really coming from." When she felt ready to find out more, she began attending sessions in Psychophonetics counseling. It is interesting to note that Jess had not used drawing at all before these sessions and discovered during this process that she had become an artist.

Biographical Concentric Layers—Imprints Frozen in Time

For people who have experienced past sexual abuse, the abuse experience continues to live on in their body-memory, in which different layers of biography live within each other like concentric circles, much

1 These "clusters of experience" were originally published in the book *Contributions to Psychotherapy in South Africa* (2003). The editor, Sylvester Madu, and the author, Yehuda Tagar, have kindly given permission for a revised version of these descriptions to be included in this book.

2 The name *Jess* is a pseudonym, and Jess has given permission for her contributions to be included in this chapter.

like the rings of a tree. The resonances of past experiences, as well as the various mechanisms with which they have survived since, are represented simultaneously. They surface into the emotional and mental processes upon typical triggers rather than in any logical or sequential order, controlling perceptions, emotional responses, interpersonal interactions, self-perceptions and the motivation for action regarding present situations.

Biographical layers are uncovered experientially during the action phase of the counseling process, which usually starts from a typical present-day adult example of the behavioral pattern in question. Through a process of sensing this moment and entering the experience through bodily sensation, gesturing the expression of the sensed experience, then letting go and physically exiting this position, a precise visualization of a biographical layer originated decades earlier can be brought into conscious awareness.

In the following description of her drawing (fig.1), Jess describes her experience of discovering layers of the past living in the present:

Figure 1: Jess—Locked in a Cage

> During our first session I mentioned to the counselor how I see myself in layers and how this was particularly evident to me during high school. This first piece was an exercise for me to "get to know and understand" these layers. The picture shows the fire is locked in a cage and needs a mighty big key if it's ever going to get out. The cage is another part of me oppressing this anger; the color coming out from the cage is the energy that's left over from this inner conflict. This energy doesn't last very long and it turns black. The result of this struggle is what I felt I presented to the outside world—a mask covering up the real me, even though I had no sense of who that was.

Excarnation—Leaving the Body When under Threat

From clinical experience and client feedback, the actual experience of most people who have experienced sexual abuse before the age of seven is that, in order to survive, their consciousness left the body so they were not fully present while it happened. It seems that children leave their bodies when they cannot process or digest the experience of what happens during sexual abuse. Consequently, they are still not fully present in the body as adults. Clients have described how they often feel as if they are not fully here, that the body feels vacant of the presence of consciousness, sensation, feeling, perception, and the ability to respond and relate to others fully. Expressed in a gesture, the person can appear empty, listless, hanging there with vacant eyes—they have gone. When this is accepted in the counseling session, it is often the first time these clients feel understood regarding the underlying pattern of their reality.

Once this experience is understood by the practitioner and acknowledged by the client and respected, there is a sense of relief in being understood and of being able to understand one's own experience in this way. Upon request, clients can always point to the direction in which they have left the body; for example, on the ceiling, behind furniture, out of the room, across the road, in the garden, always away from where the body is. They always know where they went and can describe the landscape precisely. As the counselor, we go with them physically or imaginatively to that place, to join the soul in its disembodied position; such as getting up on a chair, going behind furniture, in the garden, across the road. There comes a point where the client always stops and says something like, "This is it. That is where I went." It is a place in which they feel safe. In looking back, the client can "see" the body left on the floor of the room in the previous position. From this location, he/she feels safe enough to observe the precise position of the body. It is in this position, in the relative safety of being "out of the body" that the person can see, often for the first time, just exactly what happened. This can be very orientating and clients may need time to digest and integrate what happened. When they feel ready, the process of returning home to be present in the body can start, remembering that they are not consciously in their body, and we are joining them where they are. In the following drawing (fig.2), Jess describes how when she feels too much pain she leaves her body:

Figure 2: Jess—In Pain

> In this drawing, the woman's body and the clenched fist are mine. The little figure sitting down, pounding her fists, is me as a child. I am sitting in the area of my right ovary because this was where I had experienced pain on and off for years. The position I am sitting in (hands pounding the air and my head down), was the position I made during a session. I went "into" this pain; I was sitting down and began punching the air. It was not in a violent way, and my head was down as if I could not look at what I was punching. Again, my spiritual body is leaving me; out through my back. It has left my body but it is by no means free as it is tied up by black rope. The robots represent the disassociation I felt as a result of me leaving my body. They also represent living with chronic fatigue syndrome and the feeling of being empty and living life in an automatic mode; a feeling of not quite living.

The acknowledgement that one *is simply not fully here* is orientating, reassuring, and brings together one's concept of self and one's actual experience. Accepting, rather than judging this experience, leads to the possibility of joining the location of the departing soul physically. This can lead the client into a place of clarity, safety and orientation. From the point of view of the disembodied soul, the new step in the process can be plotted together between client and practitioner. The plotting is always about how to come back and to clear the body from the traces of invasion and to connect with the resources needed. Jess describes her experience of feeling sadness and leaving the body. The fire is her fury at being polluted by the toxic blackness, at the bottom of the picture (fig.3):

> This is the same brick wall that I had found myself looking at during a session a couple of weeks before. It was not long after revealing to my counselor about the instances of sexual abuse when I started experiencing a sadness about what happened which I hadn't been able to feel at the time. It was as if I was grieving. During the session, I had "gone into" this sadness with my whole body and my counselor asked me what I could see. We realized that I wasn't actually in my body so we went outside to find myself. We went across the road and there I was with my back turned to the house staring at a brick

Figure 3: Jess—leaving the body

wall. The small child is me and this is the brick wall. I would rather look at this than see what is happening to me during the abuse. The footprints lead to a place somewhere in my body where I came back to. A "fairy frenzy" had kept it safe. The space is safe but it is also small and confining. The black seeping up from the bottom is a poison that is threatening to taint everything.

The Imprint of Past Sexual Abuse Is Experienced as Physical Toxicity

From the experience of confronting this phenomenon many times, it can be concluded that the pathology resulting from sexual abuse is not primarily of a psychological nature, but is a phenomenon that is experienced in the body, in relation to which psychological phenomena are primarily symptomatic. To the client, the body feels contaminated, toxic, internally dirty, for many years after the abuse. Time itself does not clear this toxicity, which is the major reason people who "left their bodies" cannot fully return to be present in their body. It is as though the body or parts of it have been overtaken by a foreign presence, strange, indigestible, malignant and obnoxious, disinheriting their ability to reside in it fully. Typical expressions from clients are: "something foreign was deposited into my body, coming from the outside; it frightens me; it hurts me; it is black; I cannot stand it; I cannot stay in its presence; I cannot get rid of it; my body is no longer mine because this is present in it; I have no other body to stay in; I am stuck, half here, half nowhere; or please help me to get it out of my body so that I can come back to live in it fully."

Adult sexuality has no established counterpart in the child's constitution. The child's constitution is unable to match its energy, to break it down, digest it, or to clear it away. A toxic deposit in the subtle dimension of the bodily memory is being experienced by people who have been sexually abused, as if this was a physical toxicity insoluble by the passage of time and insoluble by just verbal descriptions of the experience. In this light, it appears all the psychological, emotional, mental, and relationship patterns acted out by people who have experienced past sexual abuse are but symptoms of a deeply entrenched experience of toxicity. Processes applicable to the embodied dimension of experience are required to break down and clear the experience of toxicity. From clinical experience, it has been found that this toxicity needs to be "washed" out of the system and the nonverbal modes of sensing, movement, visualization and sounds can be effective in doing this. Other modalities will also have their own ways of working with this. The presence of this toxicity is an actual reality for people who have experienced sexual abuse. In figure 4, Jess describes her experience of being held down and gagged:

> This piece could be placed underneath the previous one. It could reveal what is behind the seeping black poison that is threatening to taint the previous picture. Here the focus is a part of me that has been vulnerable for as long as I can remember: the digestive system. Pain in the bowel area has decreased as I gain a deeper understand-

Figure 4: Jess—feeling helpless

ing of myself. The green small intestines represent a contaminated gut, and there are little angry versions of me in the large intestine. One is trying to get out, one is asleep, and one is shouting. The flowers are being overtaken and strangled by weeds. I am being silenced by someone else's hands. The fairy is chained up and is crying because it feels helpless and unable to help me. This represents my own feeling of helplessness in the past and thinking that I will never ever be happy and pain free.

Precise Visualization: Clients Perceive the Imprint of Past Experience in Their Own Psychophysical Constitution.

Perceiving an imprint of a past experience through visualization is made possible by creating perspective in regard to one's own experience, through a process of "Enter–Exit–Behold." This process includes focusing, sensing, movement, and visualization that enable people to see their experience imaginatively, as if watching it on a screen in front of them. Precise details not only of what took place in the external sense come to light through this process, but also precise details of the internal dynamics that resulted from the event become conscious through this most central therapeutic process. People can *see* what is happening in their inner world. Jess describes her experience in which she realizes that in it she had depicted the evil eye of her assailant (fig.5):

> This picture features a window with heavy curtains. The window has an "outside" and an "inside." On the inside a purple figure sits, head down. From this point on I adopted purple to represent my physical body. I am holding the tail of my spiritual body, which has just left my physical body. From this point on big purple lips, closed eyes and a colorful tail came to represent my spiritual being. Again, fire is anger and it burns on the inside of the window. The fairy is perched on the window ledge and is attempting to protect me from what is outside the window. This space outside the window remained empty until near completion of this piece. I knew the inside of the window very well; it was the other side I had started to feel physically sick about the closer I got to it. I knew it had an "evilness" about it, I knew it was peering in and invading me in many ways.
>
> Deep down I think I knew what it was, but it was not until my next session that I mentioned it for the first time to my counselor. It was very difficult to talk about because I honestly did not think it was valid enough to be behind the rage. I told about a boy who used to live across the road from me who sexually abused me when

Figure 5: Jess—through the window

I was four or five. I told about two incidents that I managed to erase from my memory during primary school, but later returned to my memory mid-teens. Up until this stage I had little feelings about what happened and had dismissed it as something that had not had any effect on me.

The Landing Pad—A Safe Haven in the Abused Body

Psychophonetics research and clinical experience have found that the body is not completely abused, that there is a spot within the body that is not contaminated and this is how full consciousness can return to the body. Clients have often expressed in sessions that their deepest desire is to be more in their body, to be more fully present, to clear the place completely and to own their life as an expression of their true being. In the action process, many clients can visualize/discover in the observed, abused body, a spot that has not been contaminated and where their being is preserved in the body, even during the abuse. Through this spot they can start the return, to what is called: "The Landing Pad." The client visualizes this place in a specific place in the body that varies from person to person, such as in the heart, in the throat, in the middle of the forehead, inside the head, in a toe, in the belly, in the clenched fists. It is always a specific, clearly located place that the client sees as a pure, safe, beautiful color—radiant blue, green, pink, golden—and can imagine returning through it. This is the point of return.

Clients can be encouraged to re-imagine themselves as being in possession of a powerful, resilient, incorruptible place that is beyond the abuse. This realization, when becoming a direct visual experience, is very empowering for the client's sense of self. On this basis, a way can be found for ritualizing the return to the body through the pure "landing pad" in the body. Once returned, people learn to become more aware by staying in their bodies more fully. In the following drawing (fig.6), Jess describes the heart as her safe "landing pad":

> Here the contaminated gut features again. The heart is big, strong and safe and the blue represents a cleansing ritual that I worked through with the counselor. The ritual began by looking around the body for a place that was not tainted and was safe—the heart. Having found this, I proceeded to gather my fairies, strength and energy from surrounding trees to form the "cleansing" ingredients. I placed them in the heart, took them down into my gut and through my intestines, and back up through my throat and finally out of my

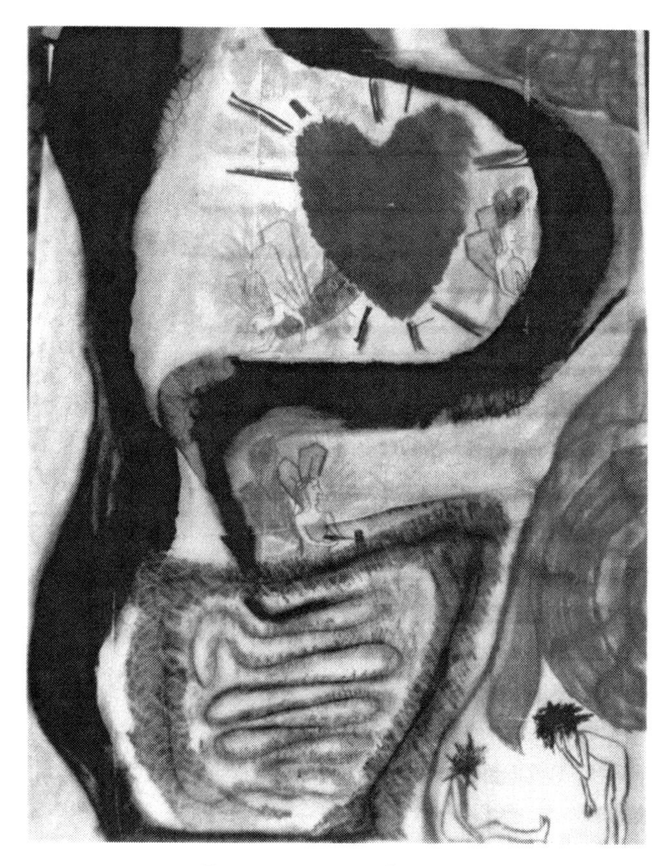

Figure 6: Jess—cleansing

mouth. I used the sound "ffffff" as I cleared my gut and the sound "gggggggg" as it left my mouth. I repeated this ritual many times. I visualized the boy from across the road being in the room now and my counselor asked me if I could protect myself. I felt strong and put my hand up to the boy "Stop!" I told him to leave the room and I watched him walk out the door: "Don't you ever come back." The two circles are my potential. The flames are no longer anger; instead, they now represent power. They are blocked off from the main image. The two figures are the facelessness and numbness I feel while being unable to step into my potential. The fairies are helping with the cleansing process, and for the first time an orange fairy appears—this is the "potential" fairy.

Summary

Practitioners need to be sensitive to the pace of the client's capacity for recovery, and not push people to open up when they are in states of high distress. It is not safe to support clients to call forth traumatic memories unless the client is able to contain the flow of his/her anxiety, emotion, memories and body sensations at will. The client's wish helps to protect the client and the counselor, especially when working experientially and during the crucial phase in the recovery. This phase includes: when the actual experience of abuse is being reexperienced; when the detached, dissociated part of oneself is safely returned to the body; the inner wound is being addressed by the caring adult presence; the disempowered component of oneself is being encouraged to take charge of the soul space and to restore safety; the deposited "toxicity" is being cleared; and when breached boundaries are mended and healed.

Preparation is needed in the recovery and healing process through a number of sessions, as preconditions need to be formed: the creation of safety in the therapeutic interaction between client and practitioner; resistances need to be owned, acknowledged and dissolved; the building and establishing of trust and safety within the client's soul, in terms of inner layers of experience coming to trust the adult intention to explore them; the creation of a higher level of coping regarding the client's current life; and the arrangement of safety in the client's social, physical, and time-management environment as he/she goes through this phase of the process. The following are typical stages in the crucial phase of the recovery process. It will vary in order and form with every person and type of issue.

The following summary illustrates the above-described elements during the crucial phase of the recovery process:

- The client establishes a clear wish relating to the emerging picture.
- Examples are chosen that exemplify a pattern from the client's present life that is in need of change, and through which the underlying issues can be externalized.
- Exploration occurs through an enter–exit–behold process—entering in gesture, exiting from this position and observing the images created by reexperiencing the chosen example from life—so that the inner dynamics can become conscious.
- Compassion Triangle—is a process of addressing the negative self-talk, self-hatred, self-resentment and putdown on oneself that have accumulated from years of suffering. Process includes exposing the negative talk, putting it in context and discovering a source of inner compassion toward oneself.
- Russian Doll—is a process of entering the inner layers of the pattern displayed in the chosen example through a number of entering, exiting and visualizing processes until the source of the pattern is discovered. It is during this process that the original trauma is likely to become exposed for direct observation and with perspective.
- Excarnation process—in the presence of reexperiencing the original trauma or even on the way to it, our consciousness departs, if that is how we learned to survive. The task is to acknowledge this experience of not being fully present, to find the direction and location of where our consciousness has gone. Joining the departed self and embodying this position has the immediate effect of our becoming more orientated, clear and present, with the ability to describe the experience.
- Staging or deep visualization—is a process of Beholding from an exited or, in this case, an excarnated position in which a clear view can be made possible regarding the actual physical situation at the moment of being traumatized. This is the time for the clearest description of what has actually taken place in the act of sexual abuse itself, as it is with some distance that it is safe to observe it. For most clients this is the first conscious meeting between the child experience and the adult awareness since the original abuse took place, often after years of repressed memories. This visualization can include a precise picture of the toxicity of the foreign energy of the adult deposited on the defenseless child body. From this perspective the client can graphically describe the colors and shapes of that deposited toxicity.

- Landing Pad—is a process of identifying in the visualized vacant body left behind a special spot inside the body, visible from the distance, into which the energy of the abuser has not penetrated. The client is asked to identify this location in the body, its color and the relative strength of that spot. This helps to forge the resolution to return to the body with new strength, via this Landing Pad and to clear it from within.
- Invoking new strength—sometimes, new strength must first be attained, imagined, practiced and acted out in preparation for the return. Internal archetypes could be created by the client, or aspects of one's higher, stronger, healthier being, previously untapped in the client's life until this moment. Sounds could also be found for the direct expression of the qualities of this new strength to be used in the act of returning to and clearing the body.
- The Return—via the Landing Pad, is done by physically moving into the "body" that was left on the floor. A solemn ritual of reunification creates a moment of great compassion and warmth, conceived and conducted by the client.
- Clearing toxins—this is done with sounds through the process of *Sound-Naming* the sound qualities that resonate with the client's experience of the qualities of the toxicity, as well as the sounds that resonate with the qualities of inner strength. These two sets of qualities, expressed through sounds, are sounded against each other with full bodily gesture, until the toxicity is cleared away.
- The advocate—the adult awareness, having embraced and defended the child, then becomes the child advocate by standing for the child in the face of the adversarial character involved in the original abuse. A ritual of authoritative dismissal can take place on behalf of the child. This ritual is sometimes called *Firing the parent,* in relevant situations.
- The guardian—either the same character as the child advocate or a special one created for this purpose—can be invoked and used to create and guard an inner space of safety that was missing or that had been breached.
- Inner child care—once the restoration of being present in the body is accomplished with the necessary protection to make the return stable, then it is time for healing, nurturing and replenishment. An internal dialogue can be established between the adult who became the child advocate and guardian and the child experience. Direct requests are

expressed by the child experience to the adult consciousness. The care and healing becomes a self-subscribed and self-applied process. For example, Jess describes how the fairy is content to look on as she, as the adult, is caring for her inner child for the first time (fig.7):

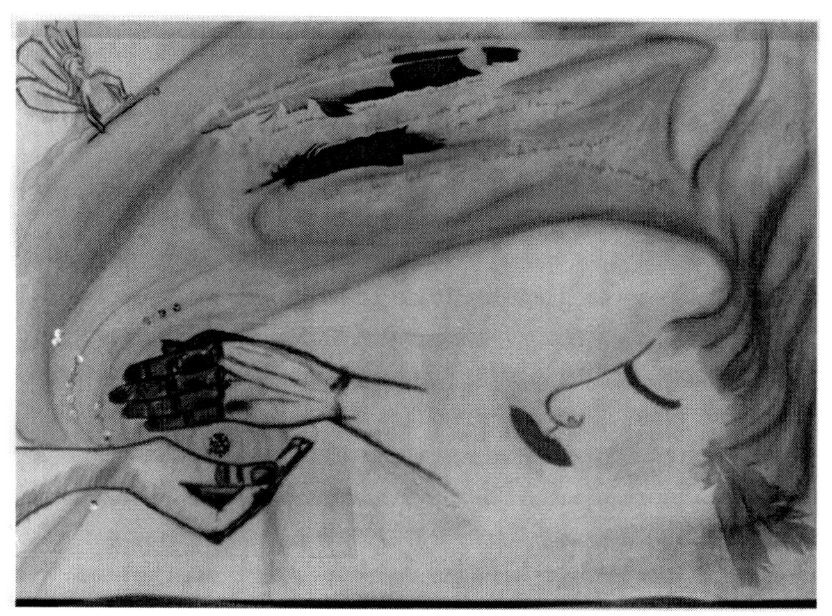

Figure 7: Jess—caring and protecting

This piece came after a session where I connected with my four/ five year old. She talked and told me she needed to cry like a child. She needed protection and understanding. Here, the purple hands are mine. I am holding and protecting a part of me, which I have shown here as my spiritual being—big purple lips and closed eyes. The words are coming from my spiritual being and are directed at the current me: "Time breeds momentum. The years have been persistent at passing, yet I have remained the same. I am still here. I can shake with rage. I can twist with pain. I can roar fire. I am not bad; I am you. Let us talk. Let me cry."

- Follow-up—in view of the internal dialogue and the caring awareness, a plan is developed for the follow-up, protection and care, for further development and maintenance of what was achieved in the sessions. A range of elements for self-care rituals and daily routines are constructed out of the material of the sessions.
- Wrapping up—at the close of each session, in view of the vulnerability of the experiences shared and of the life reality to which the client is about to return, there is a process of wrapping up, closing the protective sheaths, and consciously covering with care that which was opened up in the session.

Reflective, verbal awareness is extended to incorporate the nonverbal modes of knowing and communication, of sensing, movement, visualization and sounds. These modes of knowing help to create a bridge between the client's present adult experience and consciousness, and the client's own child experience and consciousness from the time the abuse took place. That bridge enables the client's mature abilities of caring, protecting and reassuring as an adult to be applicable to the vulnerable dimension of the client's own experience as a child. In order to heal from past sexual abuse, a tremendous level of healing energy needs to be activated, so that often people who have been through this experience become healers in their own right.

These are the main themes and clusters of meaning of clients' experiences of past sexual abuse, discovered through the therapeutic process. The intention in writing this chapter is to encourage clients to trust their own experiences and knowing, and for practitioners of other modalities in this field to become more aware of the potential of including a creative and expressive approach and to apply these findings in their own work, in their own way.

Chapter 10

Art as Expression in Illness and Pain

Arleen Hanks

Meditation

The pain we endure in life is not ours.
It belongs to our highest striving,
To another being in us
To an impulse that demands from us
To listen, turn, become and receive like children.
Pain and suffering are tools that gods use
To shape that chalice in human souls which
Ultimately must contain them.[1]

Through my work and experience as a practitioner since the mid-1990s, I have observed that pain is not a single-layered experience. Many forms of pain may be felt first as an emotion and, if not expressed, the emotion can become suppressed and then felt in other layers of our body—namely, in the spiritual, mental and emotional bodies. When further suppressed, it can become locked into the etheric, or life, body and may finally manifest in the physical body as physical illness. In the sessions described in this chapter, we will see the attempts by clients to gain this understanding through pain or illness, and, in many cases, they are set free through this pain into a

1 Beni Kleinhans is a South African Waldorf teacher who passed away in Australia after a long battle with AIDS in 1992.

new level of spiritual and/or emotional understanding in their lives. Treating any form of pain as something physical to just be got rid of without getting to the underlying emotion will be a lost opportunity for understanding. In looking deeper into the meaning behind pain, we can tap into the client's own inner wisdom.

Art in therapy is used as a form of expression for clients to express their thoughts and feelings and has been used successfully in Psychophonetics counseling sessions[2] as a way to explore the client's inner life. All experiences from our lives are held and carried within our bodies, in the living body, which can be accessed and brought into consciousness, thereby bringing about an opportunity for healing. A research study on the expression of pain through Psychophonetics counseling compared two groups. One group expressed their pain in words, the other with gesture. The level of pain was measured before and after expression, with a self-rating scale from one to ten. Statistically, 2.8 times more people reported a positive shift in their pain levels after gesturing the experience of their pain than those who just spoke about their pain.[3] This is not just limited to physical pain, as pain exists on many levels, there can also be emotional pain:

> With [Psychophonetics] counseling exercises we project emotional experiences into the corresponding sensation of the Body, and then express them through gesture and movement...Within the Subtle Bodies both [physical and emotional] types of experience take similar shapes as vibrational patterns of resonance. The process of expressing experiences through movement is equally therapeutic for physical, energetic, emotional and mental complaints.[4]

Pain exists on many levels, and can be seen as a messenger that reminds us that we are off track, that something needs our attention. There is pain of separation, pain of longing, of things unfulfilled. The

2 Steele (2005:266 & 154–155) and Birch (1997).

3 Tagar (1993).

4 Tagar (1993:98).

pain of spiritual suffering, where the soul knows it is not where it needs to be. There is the mental pain of confusion, the longing for clarity, and there is the pain of actual physical illness and wounds.

How can the application of art, specifically drawing, be useful with issues of illness and pain? I do not want to discount physical gesture and sound work, as they are integral to the whole process, however I know there are times when art can be a way for clients to artistically gesture though drawing and then freely move into physical gesture and sound. The following three case studies highlight drawing as expression in dealing with illness or pain.

Case Study 1: Penny

Penny is in her mid-fifties, a dedicated teacher who loves her work. She came to see me because she is overweight, with a rounded belly, which has been feeling "uncomfortable" and pained her, and she felt she was not being herself.

Session 1: It comes to light in the conversational phase that Penny has been looking after everyone else, but in the process forgot about herself. She is always conscious of meeting others' needs and by the end of a day finds that she has not been to the toilet or had anything to eat or drink. She feels she is losing touch with herself and her body. Penny thinks if she gets back in touch with herself and her own needs, that she will be a far better teacher. Further to our discussion, she becomes aware that she is often dissociated from the bottom part of her body, from the belly down. She discovered that it is like living in her head and looking down on her body, describing this as "watching myself from above." She decides her new aim is to be fully present in her body. She is aware that her belly needs attention, as she feels like there is a wound in there, an emotional pain. She feels her belly holds clues to her aims in life and what is stopping her achieving them. Her wish is, "To occupy my whole body, and not keep out or hold back from my belly."

In the action phase process, she says her consciousness is watching from above and she goes to this position above her body by getting up on a chair, thereby showing me where her consciousness is in relation to her body. She can see herself as being very small and hunched up over her belly, as a child. She then enters the child in gesture and discovers that the belly is empty, which is a surprise, as she was fearful of actually finding something huge, black and horrible in it.

I suggest she draw this belly, which she feels is safe and okay to do. She draws a circle of energy in yellow and red, with a space in the middle. She describes the circle as a vortex of churning energy, with nothing inside the belly. She then enters the middle of the belly, and becomes the "nothing." In this, she stands upright with arms open, smiling and then she tones with sounds. She describes this place as beautiful, calm and still, with a wave of beautiful energy coming out of the middle, calm, beautiful, and energizing. When she enters the inner place of this energy, strong pulsing waves of energy move her body and when she moves out of this position, Penny tells me that she can remember being six or seven years old, being told to be quiet, to not make a fuss. She thought that if she expressed herself, she would be too much, too dangerous. Penny changed in this process through the discovery that this inner child is also her source of fun and creativity. She is then able to give herself permission to be herself and play, by invoking her adult self who can protect. Through gesture, she holds this inner experience in the belly and makes a commitment to take care of herself. By the end of the session, Penny is standing upright and feeling present in her whole being. In the weeks that followed, she feels more present in her body and generally has more energy.

Session 2: Penny has been paying more attention to her own needs but is feeling "out of sync." She wants to engage her willpower to eat more healthily and to exercise more. Her wish is, "To get my body back again as it really is." We discuss how she sees her body as it should be, as it is in her soul point of view, to how it is physically. The *real* body is free,

Figure 8: Penny D1—a butterfly held in

fast, capable and full of energy. The current physical one is bent over and heavy. She draws how she feels about her body, after first gesturing being bent and heavy.

Drawing (fig. 8)—Penny says it looks like a butterfly and is surprised by the light and feels that the enfolding wings are holding the light in, weighing her down. As she describes the drawing, she naturally uses gesture and sounds, using her arms to do the enfolding and showing the weight by making grunting sounds. She cuts through her resistance without even realizing it, as she is gesturing, sounding and discovering what she did not see before. She found she has an attitude of having to hold the world on her shoulders, as the weight of responsibility. Focusing on the drawing again, she notices there is more tension and denseness in the base, which she explores again, entering this aspect via drawing.

Drawing (fig. 9)—In this drawing Penny says the red was the churning up, as flames, of a burning desire or will of some sort. She describes it as a big wanting, and speaks of this being her true self—the real expression of who she is being held back, and this desire in her will center to really do something. She describes a longing to do something as an expression of her real self, being connected with her spiritual self.

Figure 9: Penny D2—longing

We plot out what it would take, and she expresses fear about really expressing this desire in her belly. At this stage, she can hear herself wanting to restrict it and that it feels dangerous, yet she also wants to be freed. She is scared of the power in her belly, and when we look at the cost of not expressing this energy she realizes that, to hide it, she wears a character who is not her real self. Penny then refines her wish: "To become my real self."

Entering the process, Penny goes back to the childhood experience of being told she was too much, feeling that if she is let free she would be too much for everyone and everything, that she is somehow dangerous. She goes into gesture using the cushion to show how this experience had suppressed her. In doing this, she knows she needs safety and makes a contract with herself to bring herself into expressing who she is in her power and to be responsible. Penny then makes a drawing of radiant yellow, using art to pave a way to expression and gesture that previously she had great resistance to doing. Sounds come spontaneously, guttural sounds in the blocked, suppressed phases of the process, then opening to "Ahhs" in expressing herself, until her belly becomes full of light and radiant energy.

Session 3: Penny reports that during the week she spoke up in a meeting and expressed herself without holding back. She is excited about this and feels it as a huge step forward. She is also eating a much healthier diet, going for walks, and had gone to the toilet three times during the school day, which was a big achievement for her. She is now becoming aware of how busy she is, that she often does not say "no" when needed but keeps saying "yes" to the world. She is also noticing how she retreats into herself and into her belly (hiding), then falls back into automated behavior patterns. She notices three aspects: being in need/ in retreat, behaving in an automated way, and being the real Penny.

Penny's wish is, "To remove the automotive Penny and to learn how to deal with the demands of others in a more adult way—to be conscious—and to include myself more."

In the action phase, this becomes a process called "compassion triangle" whereby she identifies the needy self, then hears and sees the critical self, and then finds her compassionate self, learning how to be more in that position. Part of this process also involves seeing her projections, such as how she can be triggered by a certain tone of voice from another person into becoming a person who has to please others. This results in invoking more compassion to hold and nurture her inner self. After this, Penny says she now has a clear picture of this dynamic.

Comment—Initially, Penny was resistant to gesture and would retreat. However, through drawing, she was able to be more present in the body. This also gave a focus that helped her to overcome the fear, as she could see it in the drawings.

Case Study 2: Tally

Tally is twenty years old, and is facing the decision of whether to stay in Australia or go back to England. She is nervous and finds it hard to hold eye contact or communicate clearly. I saw her weekly for about two months. Drawing was a great expression for Tally as she struggles to put feelings into words. She is withdrawn, so any gesture is small and hard for her to do. However, she finds working with drawing to be freeing and revealing.

Session 1: Tally finds the close presence of people, especially men, literally painful. It hurts her physically, almost like a pain in her skin when they come too close to her. It is as if she literally has a thin skin. The result is that she pulls back and shrinks in the presence of certain people and men in particular.

Tally's wish: "I wish to have another layer and to be able to choose to let people in or out of my personal space." She chooses to focus on an event that happened the day before when someone walked into the room, in which she felt herself withdrawing, shrinking and feeling pain in her body.

Figure 10: Tally D1– cut off

Drawing (fig. 10)—Tally's drawing shows how she is cut off at the chest, by a yellow line and a ball of red pain. At that cut off, she became a small, little black person inside herself, which is clearly shown in her drawing. We use the drawings as an entry point for gesture by entering into different aspects. What becomes apparent is that she is pulling away to the left side, away from herself; she then discovers that her "I" consciousness is leaving the body/excarnating. She goes into the clouds, and in that position she describes herself as being free and wonderful, open, a beautiful blue energy, and is safe there. When she looks back to the position of where the body is, she sees that on the right of her body there is a black energy, a being of sorts, which she drew into the picture (fig. 10). She is not interested in becoming this thing, but feels safe enough to draw it. As she is only twenty, it didn't seem necessary to enter and become it at this stage. She draws a black shadow-being with a white eye that looks at her, which comes through the person. On reflection she tells how this person was a drug user.

She then remembers that this reminds her of her father, who was a drug and alcohol user and had the same feeling energy about him—she had felt the same reaction and pain in his presence when he was drunk or under the influence of drugs. There was a combination of father under the influence of drugs and the presence of the being of that drug. She felt this being would affect her energy and touch her through men, in particular those who reminded her of her father, so she became small, withdrawn and exposed in their presence, leaving the body as a form of protection, to get away from it.

Figure 11: Tally D2—blue soul

Drawing (fig. 11)—Tally feels she needs to be bigger in the presence of this type of energy. She needs to be in her full soul, she wants to have a layer between herself and "IT," needing a layer of blue—the blue of her soul, which is like the sky. She draws that and becomes it by breathing into the *sky* so to speak, toning with the sound "*OhhhIIII*" while standing very tall and upright. In the presence of the blue of her soul, the black "IT" disappears. Tally wraps her body in the blue energy and finds the pain has gone and she is able to breathe normally and sit upright. We test it by me using the sound she chose for the "IT"—something like zzssshhhhhhhjjjjj, rather insidious and penetrating—while Tally holds herself in the blue and sounds another sound: "I-D." The

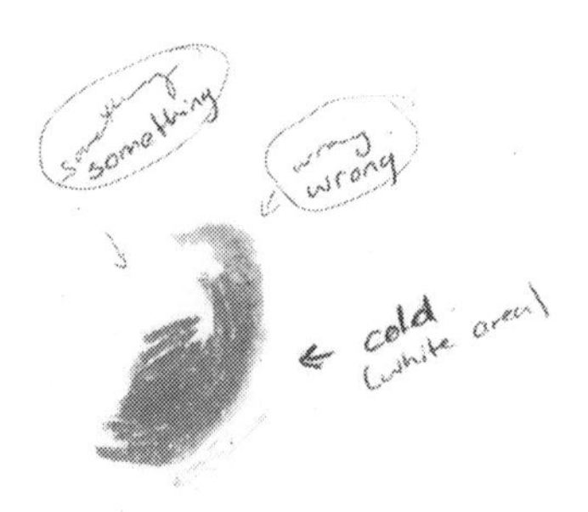

Figure 12: Tally D3—in the hip

"IT" sound and energy do not penetrate her being and she feels whole and at peace. Tally uses this at home daily and has found a huge difference when being in the presence of other people.

Session 2: In this session, Tally comments that she had noticed in the drawing of herself as a blue figure that there is a gap in the right hip, which she thinks about and notices that she is feeling pain in that exact area. She drew this in the first session and now wants to "look deeper into why there was a gap in the drawing" and why she had pain in that hip. This is Tally's wish and she begins exploring by sensing into the hip area and then drawing the experience of it.

Drawing (fig. 12)—Tally also gestures it after drawing, with her fist doing a turning motion into the other hand. In the drawing there is a white area, described as being cold, as if energy is missing and letting the cold in. Notice the missing area in her first drawing (fig. 10), which is the entry point for this session. The green area is noted as being a feeling of stretching and something is wrong with that. In the hand gesture the green area is the outer hand over the fist.

Drawing (fig. 13)—Tally enters into a second drawing, into the green area, and in this drawing she becomes aware of being stretched, feeling torn, with a tearing happening. This becomes the platform for a full body gesture, in which she feels herself going into the gesture of someone being torn between two things. On exiting and beholding,

Figure 13: Tally D4—feeling torn

she speaks of feeling torn between England and Australia. She feels unable to express the agony of being in one place while being drawn to the other, as she has just moved here with her mother and sisters. She doesn't want to let anyone down, and yet she has a boyfriend, study opportunities and friends in England.

At this point it becomes apparent that this is a decision-making process, so the rest of the session is about preparing for a three-day process. After the third day, I got a call from Tally telling me she is now clear and resolved about moving back to England to study midwifery and to reconnect with her boyfriend. This is a huge process for her, as it involves speaking her truth to her mother and sisters, which she did. They were all very supportive of her decision.

Tally's Final Sessions

In her third session, Tally faces the reality of moving back to England and facing her father. In her final session, she uses drawing to

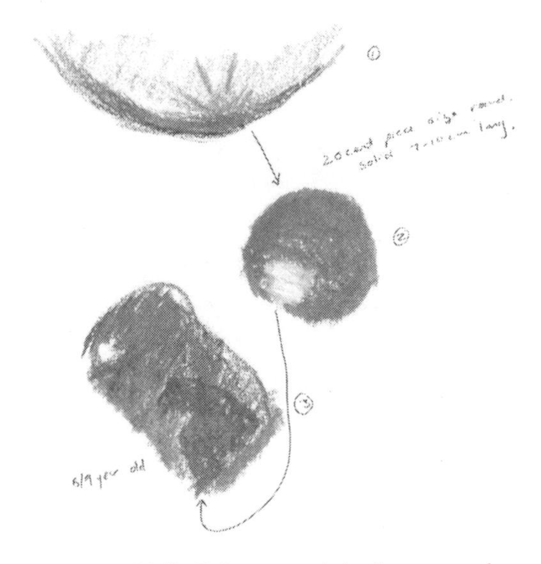

Figure 14: Tally D5—a stuck in-between place

work with an issue of blocked speaking. When she is with people and feels that she has something to say, she gets stuck, feels her throat close up and then cannot say anything. Tally speaks of hearing a very critical voice in her head when this happens, even though she knows she can do this. She feels confused by it all, and for Tally, when confusion and blocked vocal expression happens, it's a great time to draw.

Figure 14 has three drawings on the one piece of paper—the first picture is about this thing in her throat. Tally says it looks like a spiky yellow thing. She then focuses on it a bit more and draws the next picture on the same paper.

Drawing 2—orange area with a white ball in it... Tally focuses in again and there inside the orange ball is a little child sitting curled up.

Drawing 3—Tally tells me this child was eight or nine years old, is trapped and stuck in a room between her parents. Mum was on one side of the room, dad on another. For her at that age, it felt like she was being torn between them. If she sided with one she would lose and if she sided with the other she would lose—she felt stuck in this in-between place. She remembers that at the time her parents were divorced and would not speak to each other, they used her as a go-between, which meant she felt very confused and split between them. It became very dangerous to speak and she decided it was much safer not to speak and to disappear. In terms of Psychophonetics, this is an inner dynamic of an *inverted guardian* who, in this case, is trying to protect the child from the anger of her parents. The guardian pushes her speaking into the head and blocks her throat so she cannot speak.

Tally enters into the place where she disappears, where it is safe and no one bothers her. At this stage she points to drawing three (fig.14). She tells me how it is just like that in there, only it really feels nice, quiet and safe. We look at the cost of keeping quiet in her life now, acknowledging that it did keep her safe in the past. She realizes it no longer serves her and is no longer needed in her life now as an adult. To change this pattern of keeping quiet, we need to find what was missing to make it safe for her to express herself verbally. She describes how no one listened when she was younger; she was not heard, and when she did try to speak it was dangerous as there was arguing, so what was the point!

Tally says speaking is needed and what was not heard needs to be heard. She feels that she has so much to say and to express, but it needs to be safe. There needs to be a more appropriate guardian of safety. In the process of working with the inverted guardian dynamic, she becomes this in gesture with one hand over her throat and one over her head, becoming the eleven- or twelve-year-old self saying; "Don't." She then has a memory of being eight years old, playing with her cousins and finding a sick and dying bird. She was trying to help the bird but was ridiculed and became very embarrassed. The adults around at the time did nothing and just let her suffer the ridicule of the other children as she was trying to help the bird.

Drawing (fig. 15): I asked her what is missing, and she says she needs an adult who is confident and caring. She then draws what is needed. Again we have the upright blue energy that was in Tally's first session (fig.11). She immediately recognizes what this is and says: "Oh, that's

Figure 15: Tally D6—being my full self

me as I am when I am my full self." She then becomes this full self, a protective guardian, and is able to support herself in this situation. She then makes a contract with herself to protect herself in a more appropriate manner in the future and promises to support her inner expression. In this new position, Tally reenters the first position of the *story* of the session and finds she needs to speak—she then speaks as if to her father about what she had always wanted to say to him. After this, her throat feels clear. She appears calm and is sitting upright.

Comment—Tally returned to England and I have heard from her since that she did have a confrontation with her father and was able to speak her truth to him, calmly stating her point of view and needs. Through these sessions, using drawing, Tally has grown into her womanhood.

Case Study 3: Toby

These sessions use art to break through resistance in dealing with the real issue behind neck pain (whiplash). Toby is a lady in her sixties who wants to explore her experience of whiplash and hopefully to heal the pain in her neck and shoulders. I am careful to warn her that there are never any guarantees of cures of pain in working with this modality. I decide to use art as it will get her moving and doing something. She speaks of the many injuries to her neck, all resulting from whiplash in three accidents, and her wish became: "I wish to ease my pain."

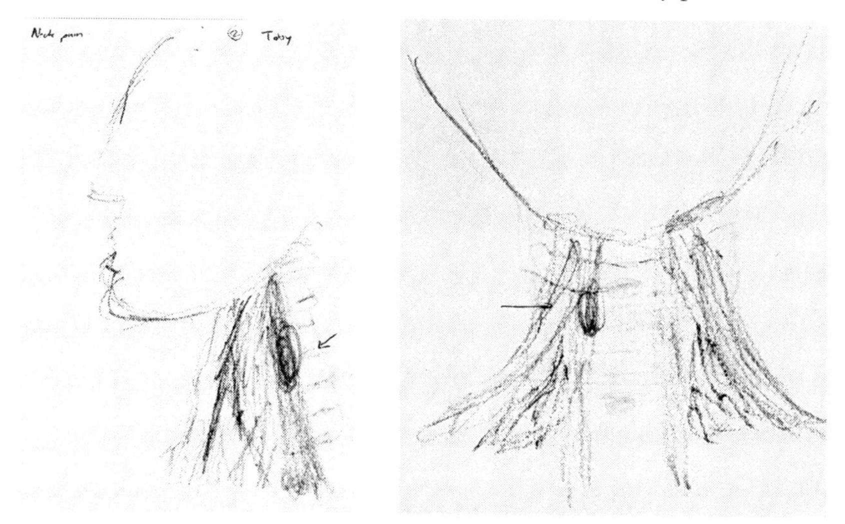

Figure 16: Toby D1—neck pain 1; Figure 17: Toby D2—neck pain 2

Drawings (figs. 16 & 17)—Drawing helps Toby to focus in a new way. Her voice changes in the process and she becomes clearer in her expression. Her first two drawings are quite technical, showing the exact location of the experience of the neck pain.

Drawing (fig. 18)—Toby then focuses on the area of pain itself and draws that experience. Her whole style of drawing changes and she enters the experience of the third drawing in gesture and finds herself screaming in despair, saying, "I am not enough, I am not being listened to, this puts me in great pain." On exiting, she sees herself as a little child without parents and without receiving the attention and love she required. She then performs a series of gestures, exploring this childhood remembering, experiencing the anguish of rejection. Even though she had parents, they were unable to be there for her emotionally and were not able to give her the love and attention she needed. This pain

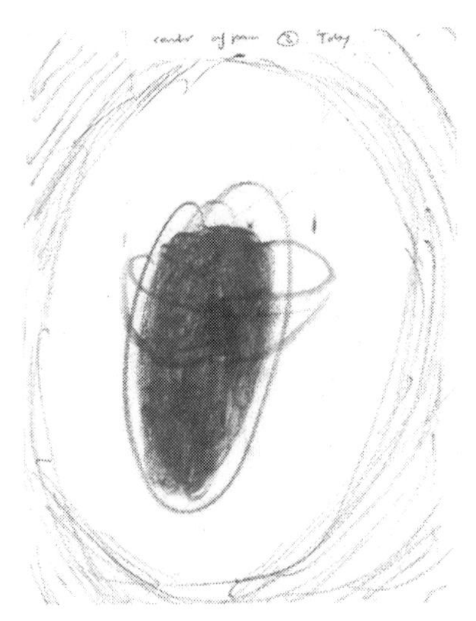

Figure 18: Toby D3—anguish

is all stored in her neck and she says she felt as a child, "I was a pain in the neck to them."

This leads to heartfelt inner work where she realizes that she has not loved herself, as at a very deep level she did not feel she deserved it. Toby invokes a much higher aspect of herself that is capable of loving this *inner child* and, in the process, her neck pain eases, using sounds as a massage. After that drawing, she is freer in her expression, with no hesitation in using gesture or sounds. After this session, Toby went back overseas to her home country to visit her family. She contacted me later to say she had an amazing reconnection with everyone and received much love from them. Her neck is easier than it was before and she uses the sounds discovered in the session to massage her neck if any pain develops. A further session was not possible due to her travel plans at that time.

Summary

Drawing is a powerful form of expression with "blocked speaking," giving a way through for clients to express themselves. When ill or in pain, drawing helps clients to gain clarity in regard to what is happening within. The subconscious surfaces through the drawings and cuts through the mental chatter, helping them to come to the heart of the matter, as the gesture of drawing is physically visible.

In researching client work in different aspects of pain and illness, I found that clients made big shifts in their various pain levels, as experienced and self-rated by each person: Toby/whiplash—there was a fifty-percent reduction of pain in one session, and she is using a sound massage process learned in the session as a way to manage any ongoing pain; Tally/hip—the pain cleared completely by end of session, but was also mixed with emotional pain which she rated as sixty percent improved; Penny's belly—this reduced in size during the sessions and emotional pain shifted to eighty percent positive improvement.

In working with art therapeutically, there are some key aspects to remember: keep an open mind with no expectations of what the client is going to do; offer art expression as a choice when relevant, so the client can feel free to express in this way; only clients know the meaning of their drawing, as it would be disempowering for the client if the therapist told them what it means or tried to interpret the drawing; doing a series of drawings is an excellent method for the process of "parachuting" into deeper inner layers, and also, laying a series of drawings out for the client to observe can be another way of gaining an overview or seeing the next step in a process. In concluding a session, drawing can help clients to encapsulate a session or to add further expression to what they have experienced; drawing can be a powerful tool to take home as a reminder picture for maintaining inner connections; and keeping a drawing journal at home can help to ground the work and to create a tangible link between sessions.

In conclusion, when working with pain in any of its forms, it helps to be mindful that there may be underlying emotional issues waiting to be addressed. We need to appreciate that pain is a warning: "The 'something wrong' can be of a physical, psychological or even spiritual nature"[5] and understanding the difference between these aspects

5 Gawler (2001:81).

is fundamental in dealing with pain appropriately. Artistic expression through such mediums as clay, painting and drawing are powerful ways of entering into these aspects and moving beyond sensory experience. Experience created with our own hands can offer opportunities for deeper connections, for knowing to become visible, and for healing to be possible.[6] I hope the reader will find this way of working worthwhile, and that it encourages others to use drawing and other artistic means, as ongoing practices in their lives.

6 Steele (2005).

Chapter 11

Transforming Anger through Clay Work

Anne Holland

Fortunately, the abyss on the edge of which man lives, the abyss opening out before him in religion and cognition, can be bridged.... It is here that art enters. It forms a bridge across the abyss. That is why art must realize that its task is to carry the spiritual-divine life into the earthly; to fashion the latter in such a way that its forms, colors, words, tones, act as a revelation of the world beyond.[1]

Artistic expression through clay in Psychophonetics counseling sessions is a powerful tool for transforming and healing, especially as a way of working with anger. In the counseling process the counselor provides a space for clients to enter into a deeper and more conscious relationship with themselves, where they can develop their capacity for expressing their true being. The medium of clay can further enhance and deepen the client's experience. As a practitioner, I have been exposed to a range of experiences in the arts, not only to foster my own personal and spiritual growth and development but also to develop my capacity for empathy and visualization, to enhance my understanding of the client's experience and to enable an accurate and sensitive response to the information the client has shared.

1 Steiner (1964); lecture 4, para. 7/8.

Generally, psychology has invested insufficiently in creativity, whereas research shows that the creative person has the following characteristics: optimism and confidence, acceptance of ambiguity and uncertainty, a wide range of interests, flexibility, tolerance of complexity, verbal fluency, curiosity, drive and persistence, independence and nonconformity or reasonable risk taking.[2] The beauty of the Psychophonetics approach is that it invites both counselor and client to use their creativity, to imagine the future possibility of the client's self that is waiting to be formed.

Several years ago, I found the possibility of using creativity as an additional tool for expression within a counseling session potentially exciting but also challenging. Firstly, I had to begin with myself, and initially my own lack of any experience with artistic expression made the task quite daunting. As I began to experience the benefits of expressing myself and creating forms in clay, not only did my creative skills develop, but my ability to imagine and visualize did, too. To express myself creatively and artistically was empowering. It was inevitable that I would extend the use of these tools into my work with clients. The movement of the hands in the clay was another form of gesturing. The clay invites whole-hand movements, which encourage expression of feeling and bypasses the control of the thinking mind. It seems to activate even deeper forces from within through the act of shaping the clay into something new.

As the use of clay encourages the development of more subtle feelings and has the capacity to create resistance as well as lending itself to refinement, I became interested in stimulating the creative imagination by using clay in the therapeutic context. I found it could lead to deeper expressions of the client's feeling and will, and provide an avenue for clients to face deeply entrenched patterns of behavior, thus allowing for the creation of new possibilities in their lives.

Working collaboratively with clients to create their "wish" is crucial. This is where clients express a desire to change something within

2 Egan (2002).

them. It is here that client and counselor agree to look at the inner dynamics of the client's experiences. This stage of the session harnesses the clients' will, as their conscious choice to face an aspect of themselves. In the action phase of a typical Psychophonetics session clients will be asked to gesture, that is, show with their hands what is happening inside their body. Then, through gesturing this experience with the whole body (Entering), clients can reach their inner self and express what is being held within the physical body. Then they can step back from that position (Exiting) and from a distance can look at what they have gestured (Beholding); thus, they are able to see their own inner dynamic projected in front of them. In this activity, the human body is seen as a map for the human psyche, through which aspects of our inner life can be traced and observed in full consciousness.

Using clay as a form of gesture in the action phase of a session is useful for clients who are locked into a strong, repetitive pattern of behavior, especially where anger and/or fear cannot be expressed. Clay provides a release for clients who previously may have resisted expressing anger and are not connected with their underlying hurt feelings or blocked speaking. The combination of the properties of clay and the activation of the creative imagination can provide a deeply transformative experience that can lead to a high level of inner resourcing and expression of the will.

Ken—is a forty-eight-year-old English migrant who came to counseling because he was having difficulty in his current relationship, which is relatively new. He feels scared about the possibility of losing the relationship and, at the same time, he is constantly angry with his girlfriend and intimidated by her friends. During the previous five sessions he had responded positively to the use of drawing and had enthusiastically done a number of drawings at home to consolidate the work done in the sessions. It was clear that expressing himself creatively added a deeper dimension to his experience.

On arrival for his fifth session, he is very angry and his whole body is consumed by hatred. The incident that triggered his anger had occurred the previous evening, when he had dinner with his girlfriend and her friends. He had left the party in a rage and had worked himself into a place of absolute hatred and a desire for revenge. He is in such reaction to these people that he has no perspective because he is so flooded by emotion, and says, "I want to stop being so angry all the time." When provided with a ball of clay he pummels and works with it until it is completely flattened out and his energy is spent. The amount of energy that he pours into the clay is enormous and releases him from the grip of anger. The movement of his hands in the clay is a powerful gesture that enables him firstly, to express the inner dynamic he is experiencing onto the clay. Secondly, he is able to separate himself enough from it to become more present and to see that his heart is being completely squashed. Beholding his squashed heart leads him to enough perspective to understand how hurt and frightened he had felt.

He then goes into a place of deep feeling, where he quietly sobs, until eventually he is able to speak and talk about how his father used to beat him and how angry and frightened he had been as a child. As he remembers himself as a seven year old, he understands that not only did he as a young boy have every right to be upset and angry but also that he was not bad. From this place, he is able to nurture his inner boy. As he relaxes and gains perspective, he becomes a more compassionate adult who can see the dynamic that had been operating in him the previous day and, of course, often in his adult life. He realizes that when he felt intimidated, inadequate and stupid around well-spoken people, he became the angry seven-year-old again who wanted to lash out and hurt someone. At this point Ken makes another wish: "I wish to look after the little boy," and a process follows to address this.

The clay enables Ken to explode his imploded reaction, to safely express his anger and fear from within. This leads to him remembering the brutality of his father and thus finding the wounded child within. He is also able to see how this reaction was triggered and become able to connect with his compassionate self. The hurt feelings and blocked speaking are finally acknowledged and the "I," or self, is able to express itself. In this creative process, Ken moved through a number of processes and the transformation that took place within Ken in this session provided me with the incentive to use clay more regularly with clients.

The above case also shows that the sheer physicality of the clay is a medium that men in particular feel comfortable with. It is a medium that creates the equivalent of a series of very deep gestures—it can be pounded or thrown onto a board, leaving an exact visual imprint of the anger and its impact. It certainly takes clients into a very deep place and liberates them from the constraints experienced in just talking about it. I have observed that, while male clients were working with the clay, pounding and shaping it, this often leads them to identify and become able to talk about their hurts and fears—while being actively engaged in an activity. It is through creativity that they could access deeply buried aspects of themselves.

To consciously choose to deal with our own reactions, particularly anger, takes considerable will. To deliberately cut through our own layers of defense to access something that is usually not acknowledged, requires considerable self-knowledge and a great deal of courage. To be able to move from blaming others to owning our own darkness is to claim more of our own soul life and spiritual truth. This action requires not just men, but women also, to break through the socialization of generations to find new and improved ways of expressing hurt feelings.

Brigid is a sixty-year-old migrant woman who came to Australia when she was six years old. She is divorced, has no children, lives alone and is crippled with arthritis in her legs. She walks with a walking stick and can barely get up the step into my house. She has recently lost her job and now has to go to Centre-link. She was referred to counseling by a homeopath, who was concerned about her being depressed.

During the previous four sessions she had dealt with her anger toward her former husband, from whom she had separated many years earlier. He was an alcoholic and violent. She was unable to have children, and in-vitro fertilization did not work. She believes that he blamed her for not being able to have children. Most sessions she cries without being able to say what she is feeling or why. She does express her anger toward her ex-husband, and yet her health indicates that her body is still crippled with rage. She mentions in passing that her mother had become ill with tuberculosis on the trip to Australia and had spent the next three years in a sanatorium, so the children had been put into an orphanage. They were given no information about where their mother was and they hardly saw their father.

In this fifth session, she describes for the second time her frustration with Centre-link and the humiliation she feels there. She talks about how powerless and small she feels there and how they show her no respect. She has always been employed and feels proud of her ability to look after herself financially. She recognizes that she went there with anger locked up inside her and that she was probably unfriendly and rude to her case manager, who is very young. She describes feeling as if she was back at school, which makes her feel very hot in the chest and her lips very tight. She feels trapped and wants to escape, acknowledging that when she was at Centre-link, she was very shut down. She can see that she shuts people out and the cost to her is that people are unlikely to help or show her any respect. She recognizes that she is often battling alone without much support, particularly from her family. Her wish is: "I wish to be able to go to Centre-link, and be fully present."

She senses into her body and immediately begins to flatten the clay with her hands. She takes some time and eventually stands up so that she can press down on it even harder. She becomes very strong and does not resemble the woman whose legs can barely hold her up. Eventually she stops and exits this place of suffering and anger. On beholding the clay, she names it "Feck off," which she says in a most uncharacteristic snarl. The release of anger through her gesture into the clay leads her to seeing the pain and anger she has been holding in. From the beholding position, she remembers being in the orphanage and how she was terrified because she hadn't wanted to go into a classroom without her sister. She says she is seven years old, that she had a number—she was number 58. It was like being a prisoner. Her mother was at the sanatorium but

Brigid was too little to go and see her. Eventually her aunty looked after the kids, but she "pissed off" and left them with their father, who worked and paid them little attention.

She is very moved remembering this experience, crying with deep feeling. She says that her inner little girl needs love, protection, reassurance, attention, guidance and a home. When asked who has these qualities for the inner girl she immediately thinks of her older sister. She describes her as being trustworthy, gentle and strong. She stands up and invokes this energy with the sound "*mah*" and the color blue with which she nurtures the little girl, holding her in her heart. She then speaks what she wanted to say, and couldn't at the time, to the people in the orphanage. She says in a clear, strong voice, to leave little Brigid alone, as from now on she will look after her. At the end of the session, she rehearses what she wants to speak to her case manager. Shortly after this session, she had to attend a meeting with her case manager and was able to approach her in a relaxed and friendly manner.

Brigid finally found the compassion and the protection for her inner child, who had been neglected. By exploding her imploded reaction in the clay she gained enough perspective to see that the survival mechanism she had developed as a very frightened child in the orphanage was still a response she used as an adult when scared or angry. By unblocking the hurt feelings and the rage, she was able to speak up for herself. The lack of presence she often felt in her life meant that she endured a brutal marriage for many years, and although she was angry and hurt, she had just put up with things. Brigid's case demonstrates how clay can be a safe, useful and effective substance for visually appreciating how anger can appear.

Several years ago, I observed that some of my male clients, in particular, had difficulty expressing anger in the counseling sessions. In trying to understand what the inhibitors were for them, I began looking at what I could do as a female counselor to assist these clients to deal with their anger. I found that as their trust grew during the sessions, their willingness to expose their vulnerability increased. It needs to be stated that anger is not necessarily a problem, as it can be a natural human response that helps us to survive or protect others and ourselves, or it may motivate or inspire us to be more vibrant and alive, to deal with injustice and to take action. However, many people have been taught that anger is bad and even evil, and for many, their experiences of anger while growing up were not positive. This may mean that anger becomes disowned so that it takes on a life of its own and may become aggressive behavior; or be projected onto others; or anger can be turned inward, to become imploded anger, with depression as a probable outcome.

These male clients revealed a great deal about themselves, including issues such as sex addiction, poor sexual performance, grief of the loss of their children, sexual abuse as a child, frustration at work, confusion about their relationships with women, disappointments and confusion about their careers, as well as their hopes for the future. However, I noticed that these men would get to a certain point in feeling anger, begin to express it and then would stop. I initially thought it may have something to do with my attitude to men and anger. I knew that as the counselor, I had to be comfortable with anger and be able to take responsibility for any confusion I may have about their anger, to be able to identify any reactions I may have to a client expressing anger.

When they pummeled or kicked a cushion to do an initial release of anger, with the intention to explore its underlying dynamics, I could see that they would suddenly stop, then collapse and give up. I could sense their disappointment and frustration at missing the release of that energy that was clearly stored in their bodies. I also sensed their fear of letting it go. What became apparent was that these male clients were reluctant to let go completely, because it would be done in front of a woman, and because they also feared losing total control. All these men said they had experienced times in their lives when they had expressed anger inappropriately and had experienced the consequences as rejection, shame and self-loathing. To consciously choose to deal with anger takes considerable will. To cut through layers of defense deliberately to access something that is usually not acknowledged requires considerable self-knowledge and a great deal of courage. This action requires a man to break through all the socialization of generations because in many ways, anger and aggression are an acceptable part of masculinity. These clients expressed shame about their anger when they talked about the incidents in their lives. They were aware they had not found a way of expressing it legitimately or consciously in life. In my reading, I found that shame and bullying are the ways boys are coerced into conforming to the masculine cultural norm. In conforming to this narrow definition of masculinity, boys lose a part of themselves and the grief of this loss can lead to anger, depression and loneliness in adulthood.[3] Through considerable experimentation, I discovered that men are more likely to express their hurt feelings and anger and indeed transform themselves by using drawing and/or clay within a Psychophonetics counseling session. They could begin to identify issues nonverbally, which allowed them to go deeper than they had done previously through just conversation. Building on conversation and a wish, the anger can be legitimately and safely dealt with.

Some clients have flattened the clay with such intensity that they exploded an imploded reaction, which they had previously resisted. If it is very difficult for a client to explode their anger in a gesture or into clay, they may be encouraged to throw the clay onto a hard surface (e.g., floor, wall, or board). It is important to encourage the client to take the time to practice so that the clay is thrown hard for a full explosion to be embodied and expressed effectively. By doing this, the client unravels the imploded reaction and through this organic process, can find the vulnerable aspect. Thus the clay provides a means of expressing deeply entrenched responses to life, and can release a block in the heart, freeing clients from the tyranny of their emotions. The expression in the clay empowers them and leads them into their inner chamber, where they are able to understand the source of their persistent behavior. From this new perspective, there is the possibility of gaining control of their response, by taking care of their hurt feelings and being able to

3 Obsatz (2003).

speak what needs to be spoken and expressed. Some clients then move into connecting with their inner resources using clay, while several clients have created something new in the clay, which became a resource they could draw on in life. Once they have seen the forces that were impeding their lives, as expressed in the clay, they move organically into creating something that is new and positive.

Jack was in conflict with his boss, and in the session he creates a large, mountainous shape in the clay. This is his boss. He then proceeds to make ten small figures, and one is tiny. He says that they are like a family, but he knows that they are actually aspects of him and the little one is a baby. I observe that they all seem to have their backs to the boss. He then slowly and deliberately turns each one around to face her, at the same time he pulls them in much closer to each other, so that the baby is now completely protected. He then slowly and deliberately begins to tear the mountain figure into small, flat pieces, which he spreads out across the table and describes as the waves of an ocean. He had reclaimed his power by first expressing and observing the destructive reaction, then guarding, protecting and transforming his inner soul dynamics.

The tactile property of the clay enables clients to sense deeply into their own body, bringing their blocked feelings out into the clay. The gestures made into the clay are a fast track to the inner chamber. The clay and the instinctive, intuitive act of creativity required to shape the clay, appear to activate their higher will, thus releasing the clients from their persistent reaction enough to be able to see it and then to consciously do something about it.

Tom is forty-two years old, from a non-English-speaking background and is studying toward changing his career. He has come close to dropping out of the course and has been looking at his issues around commitment. He is single and has a history of superficial relationships with many women. I have seen Tom intermittently over the last two years, and recently he came back for a series of sessions.

In one session, he had been having headaches, and had taken a week off from his course because he wasn't coping and felt that his life was out of control. His headaches have been numbing and often led him to feeling frightened of death. He queries whether there is something wrong with him. The common picture in the conversation phase became a sense that there was "something" unknown yet very tender within. He senses the tenderness in his solar plexus and says that he cannot go there. He describes it as a delicate situation. He is very moved by the possibility of the tenderness. His wish is, "I would like to experience what is so tender and inexperienced."

Tom senses into his body, and remembers feeling troubled by death. He makes a series of shapes with the clay. He moves organically from the first one to the next one, totally absorbed in the creation of the figures. He talks about them as each is completed. The first shape that he forms is of his heart. It is rough inside and hollow. He then creates a flower that he says sits on the crown of his head and has an opening to something divine. The next shape he describes as being of the gesture of the "I." The figure is standing with one arm up and the heart is open. It represents both surrendering and receiving. Suddenly he realizes that his heart is not defended, but is whole. The next figure is of a contorted body, and he says it represents the inner dance between receiving inspiration and then knowing how to use it. The next shape is round and hollowed out, and inside there is nothing. He tears some clay into pieces. He says, "They are fragments...heaps of broken pieces." He describes it as "a wasteland." He sees wasted time, a wasted life. He cries and says, "it's so tender," and sees himself at five years old. He is totally in feeling and he talks about feeling lost over the last three years, of how he wanted to belong in his family. He is surprised by this, as he had not realized that he did not belong, and he talks about the difficulty of belonging to two cultures. He looks at the broken pieces and says, "I need open heart surgery, like lightning, so I can connect to my spiritual self." He makes a new wish: "I wish to connect to the spirit self and live in the connection."

To find the connection using clay, he creates a figure with both arms raised above its head and open to the heavens. He then creates a little boy, but says, "my heart needs to be safe." He realizes that before a connection can be made with spirit, the little boy needs to be safe. He creates a smooth ball and strokes it a lot using a nurturing "*mmm*" sound. He then makes the child's heart and sits quietly sounding "*mmm*," feeling the connection in his heart. In this process, Tom uses the expression of his creativity in clay as a means of facing and then healing the fear of his own spiritual self. By using clay to engage deeply with this fear, he is able to activate inner resources. This process allowed Tom to move beyond his usual defense mechanism that usually involved lots of talking.

Through this approach, a safe environment can be created for men (and women) to transform anger through the creative medium of clay. My own experience of these sessions has been very powerful, as I, too, have been liberated. I now feel safe and confident in encouraging men to express their anger and rage. It also led to me having a better understanding of my own ways of dealing with anger. The act of creativity supports the awakening of one's own potential. Clay in particular is a deeply felt medium which allows the etheric life forces to be expressed and become available for healing, especially when the intuitive capacity of the feeling will is activated, clear from any astral activity (e.g., emotional reactions) impinging on the etheric life.

Revisiting deeply held memories in the life body provides the opportunity for bringing aspects of the unconscious self into consciousness. It is here that transformation becomes possible. Working with the three-dimensional property of clay encourages the coming together of aspects of the self that are often separated. Through this activity, clay provides a medium for a soul gesture to be expressed, "Creating through clay or drawing *makes* me, and *through it* I *become*, which means that releasing expression/speaking is a powerful "I am" gesture."[4]

4 Steele (2005:266).

In summary, the therapeutic use of clay is helpful for those clients whose creativity has been squashed, as a means of being safely introduced to their own creativity and its healing potential; for clients who have trouble expressing anger; for clients, particularly male clients, and others who come from a migrant or working-class background that does not encourage expressions of feelings; for clients who use talking as a way of avoiding the expression of their feelings; and for clients who are on the threshold of a major turning point in life. Using clay in this way ensures that the client has a whole-body experience in a safe way, while allowing full embodied release and expression and providing an opportunity for the client to be completely absorbed in an activity in which the mind, the heart and the physical body are completely integrated.

Creativity is activated by the act of shaping a piece of clay with both hands. In the process of being totally absorbed in the interaction with the clay, the heart is opened and the controlling mind is bypassed. In clay work, there are the transformative qualities through destruction and creation, as expressions of speaking that can engage thinking, feeling and willing organically in the activity. Finally, the creative, artistic medium of clay leads beautifully into the Psychophonetics processes, as the methodology is able to incorporate a wide range of creative activities that allow the deepest expressions of the soul and spirit. In the act of creative expression, clients using clay reach toward a more conscious and aware state that provides them with the chance to live their lives more fully.

Chapter 12

The Character of Marijuana Craving and Its Impact on the Healing Process

Jillian Fowler

In this chapter my interest and counseling work in the area of addiction is focused on four clients who were habitual users of marijuana, using a Psychophonetics approach to addiction as a framework. After defining addiction as used in this study, I will outline the needs that the clients felt were met by the drug, set against those from the literature, and the underlying needs the clients discovered after entering deeply their experience through the body. All clients entered into the character of their craving verbally, while two of them chose to explore it more deeply as part of their intention for healing their addiction.

We will examine three aspects of the craving: verbal understandings, the state of the client, and the character or astral entity of the craving. The discoveries of the latter will be the focus of this chapter, concentrating on similarities in content and character of the craving. We will discuss the impact of exposing and confronting the entity, and the opportunities for healing made available through this process. Then we will draw implications in terms of expressing and strengthening the self, releasing will forces and developing connections with spirit, and make reference to their importance in the recovery from marijuana addiction in the context of its particular characteristics and effects compared with other addictions, substances and drugs.

This study involves two male and two female volunteer participant clients, ages twenty-two, twenty-nine, forty-two and forty-five years, who attended a number of sessions, varying from one to eight, each session lasting approximately an hour and a half. In keeping with the phenomenological, organic nature of Psychophonetics, and by honoring the premise that clients determine the content and direction of their work, sessions dealt with issues the clients chose. The focus of the work was with finding alternative, effective ways, internally and externally, of meeting the needs, both conscious and underlying, for which the drug was used as a substitute. Clients explored emotional issues to varying degrees, largely dependent on their intentions and emotional readiness. The focus chosen for this chapter is on the "beast" or "astral entity" discovered in the craving for marijuana. It has not been referred to in relevant literature, unlike the other two aspects of the craving we will explore more briefly. However, Yehuda Tagar, in his work on addictions, has mentioned it in relation to smoking cigarettes.

Background Definitions of Addiction/dependence

The definitions of addiction can vary markedly, from the broad and inclusive, for instance: "an increasingly compulsive urge to suppress conflicts through outside stimulation of any kind to displace what otherwise can only be solved by one's conscious effort"[1] which many people can easily identify with, to more specific and bounded definitions where a distinction is made between substance abuse and dependence, which refers to full-blown addiction and is more severe.[2] For the purposes of this study, the writer refers to *drug dependence*, *addiction* and *habitual use* interchangeably—the working criteria being that each of the four clients had "used" more than weekly over more than four years, and had been through periods of trying to desist and relapsed. They were at different phases of their engagement with the drug, varying within the

1 Felicitas Vogt (nd:9).

2 Bloch and Singh (1995:174–175).

contact period between about twice daily and once a fortnight at the commencement of contact.

Findings

Needs the Drug Came to Meet—Verbal and Experiential

A table of the needs the drug came to meet, according to participants, set against those referred to in relevant literature, is included in the appendix. In this, a separation is made between the needs acknowledged verbally and those discovered as the result of a deeper exploration into bodily awareness, made possible with Psychophonetics counseling. One can infer or begin to gain an impression of the character of the craving from examining the differences discovered with this mode of exploration.

Character of the Craving Force

On closer examination, the character of the craving when explored more deeply can be seen in two aspects:

1. The inviter, or state of the requester. This becomes visible on examining the inner needs exposed. A wounded, or victim part of self is clearly present.
2. The one between who delivers—the astral entity. The latter is the one who often stays hidden, or may at most be hinted at only in deep conversational counseling, and can clearly be distinguished, experienced and understood with the nonverbal tools employed in Psychophonetics.

The Craving Force—Verbal

References to the craving force by participants during the conversation phase were:

> *Client 1:* "a gravitational pull," describing it as though he was like a fish drawn to the bait, and at other times, as a friend offering close connection and consolation.

Client 2: the promise of seduction by an effective, welcoming lover—strong attraction, the promise that he would fix everything and offer an adventure, which she loved. A good and skilled lover who in the end is bad for you, brings out a sneaky, rationalizing part of her.

Client 3: very tricky, manipulative, luring promise of connecting, warmth and love, often referred to with a light in his eyes, which implied fun and excitement.

Client 4: "a seducer, a trickster, a tease that gently lures me," insidious, "its tentacles envelop me." It offers the promise of new and original discoveries. At another point, she says, "it hooks into me and I lose part of myself."

All the clients identified the duplicit nature of the craving in their descriptions—and referred to their ambivalence toward it—the sense that it was an effective, if enticing friend, promising satisfaction, and inferring there was a downside.

Deep Exploration and Confrontation with the Craving Force

Client 1: Although he chose to enter the deeper dynamics in his body around dope smoking, he did not discover the craving entity experientially. He was resistant to entering the wounded little boy he could see so clearly. He saw and welcomed the dynamic of the drug coming to protect him from difficult feelings held in the wounded one—he chose to stay behind the wall he constructed and the drug reinforced. He became aware that he was still colluding with the drug and what he saw as the easy way out. His internal resources and the costs of this defense needed to grow, to motivate him to deal with the pain.

Client 3: After the first Conversational counseling session, he chose not to proceed with subsequent sessions on marijuana, saying this was no longer an immediate issue in his life; he preferred to work on relationship issues involving a woman to whom he was deeply attracted. Given one of the main needs the drug came to meet for him was feeling loved, this may have been another point of entry to similar underlying dynamics brought to light as an opportunity for his further growth and healing.

The next section focuses on the inner experience of the craving force as discovered by the other two clients who elected to go there as part of their recovery process. Although these aspects of the craving mentioned above were still apparent to some degree, other more sinister aspects became apparent:

Client 2: Decided to explore more deeply the craving sensation—the urge to smoke a joint when it came up in response to anxiety she felt during the session. She senses deeply into the sensations in her body, gestures their movement and separates from them, to observe (enter–exit–behold). She reports that she is being pushed down from behind: "IT is trying to hold onto me—IT has the power." She discovers further, by becoming the force onto a cushion, that it is pulling down over her heart, squashing it. She experiences it as very big and forceful. She says it needs lots of power—it stops her from achieving her potential—from developing and contributing, stopping her seat of power, her heart. For her, her heart was like her kernel.

Staging: She sees that it has bad intentions and describes it as "humanoid"—charcoal grey, plastic, hairy, bark-like skin with very large hands. Although she says it is not human, it became more humanlike as she works with it. It is much more scary and sinister than her subsequent drawing (fig.19) portrayed, which was drawn after the session, and after she had confronted it, when its initial extreme sinister quality had already reduced. When asked whether it had a heart, to distinguish whether it was a part of her or a foreign entity, she says she believes everything has, but this one was shrunken, no good. Once she sees its influence, she has more perspective and expresses the fear that "IT"/him will mobilize his forces to defeat her. She feels not strong enough to defeat him alone, yet she expresses the desire to do so.

Resourcing—She feels the fear in her body but is able to express it sufficiently through the bamboo process until she can imagine, connect with and bring the qualities of spiritual light and love to her heart. She breathes them in and turns courageously to face "him,"

Figure 19: Client 2 (D1)—Humanoid

being full of loving strength, and she bursts out laughing: "HE has shrunk." Once her love was directed toward him, he became harmless. She creates this as a bubble of protection in which she says she feels strong and alive. There was a palpable sense of triumph in the air, with no craving.

Summary comment (Client 2)—This client discovered a lot about the power and qualities of her craving. In this instance, the character of the craving altered dramatically, from the seductive lover mentioned earlier, to that of a menacing enemy once it was seen, experienced and thoroughly explored on the inside. She moved from the illusion of seeing herself as being in charge of the decision to smoke at first, to seeing the urge brought in by a foreign, unfriendly force from behind her. It threatened to overpower her and shut down her truth in her heart center. She became more conscious and her will to do something about it was fired by her desire to come from her own truth as expressed in her wish. She summoned her spiritual resources to counteract its power, bringing love to bear, to dissolve and protect herself from the negative power of the craving (fig.20).

Figure 20: Client 2 (D2)—Loving strength

Client 4: This client chose to revisit the craving to understand it more deeply. Once seeing it clearly in all its complexity, she chose to integrate the learning and healing she had done in the previous sessions and further resource herself with what she needed to thwart its power. She chose to connect with the craving force through sensing into her body and then drawing the process. First, she recognizes that the force could enter her in one of two instances:

1. most commonly, when she felt bad—when it felt like she was in shock—and raw, it pushed her, there was a jolt, a surprise, and it offered relief, relaxation and connection with self and others, and at best, the universe; or
2. when she felt she had been good or felt good, it enticed and twisted her, reassured her she had done good work, and was centered, she deserved a reward—beckoning her sweetly—she named this as a seductress, a lure.

She chose to enter this latter experience because it was less conscious and therefore less controllable for her at this stage. There was a process she represented on three connected sheets of paper (Fig 21).

Figure 21: Client 4 (D3)—Interacting forces

The gentle enticement, represented by pale peach color and gentle curves, leading to a flirting with the idea, reaching out to meet it with brown curly lines—resisting, followed by a struggle, represented by a kernel of black and brown—accompanied by lots of conflicting thoughts and feelings—a game, an intrigue—including feelings of excitement, being on the edge, her rebellious self ignited—and a twisting in her thinking: "I'm a free spirit, and I'll go with it rather than against it." Another, wiser part of herself drawing her back: "Don't go there." Suddenly, a big, black, grasping claw appears, seemingly from nowhere: "Fucking shit, I'll get you, you bitch. You're trash anyway." She feels herself deflating, crumbling, being drawn down into the black cesspool and giving up...which makes her think, "Fuck it; I'll just give in and get smashed anyway."

She vividly portrays these four aspects of self interacting with the force, which increasingly became grasping, evil, and derogatory, and ended up feeling a pulse in her tummy, heaviness in her heart, weak and lifeless in the black cesspool. There is a small, black dot encircled in it. What was that? She responds with "hope," and when asked what she could do to heal the situation, she knew. She can nurture herself and grow from there. She went on and drew a green shape similar to the whirlpool, slowly, gently, lovingly expanding, describing the accompanying sense of peace and tranquility, gently rubbing her fingers almost sensuously over the lines. She says she feels wonderfully relaxed, at peace.

Reflecting on the process and discussing how she could move from one state to the other in future, she chose to bring the green, nurturing quality in at an earlier point. This represents the presence of the archetypal *wise woman* full of compassion, whom she had invoked to care for herself in a previous session, when experiencing abandonment by her mother as a baby. "The Great One," as she calls her, is able to hold her firmly, yet lovingly, gently drawing out her tension; her jumpy tummy is dissolving in the ripples of the water, of the warm bath she imagines as bathing her. She is submerged deeply in the sensuous warm touch of the water, using her breath, focusing on the tension in her neck and shoulders and breathing it away, feeling clear and relaxed.

She discovers then that she can create and activate that dreamy inspirational space where she can be in touch with her own creativity and truth, as the connection she yearns for and had previously only experienced via the dope. She judges this scenario; she creates herself as much superior to what she describes as: "falling for or into the lure" of the dope and suffering the subsequent weakening, hangover, loss of energy and direction (cited by all four clients).

Summary comment (client 4)—Her experience exposed the character of the craving as illusory and deceptive in two important ways:

1. That those tendrils or gentle enticement—referred to as the seductive, luring, pulling, warmly inviting force by others above—were not her friends, but held something far more sinister behind them, and
2. that it was not she but "IT" who had been in charge of her decision to smoke (as in the previous example); all that was left of her was a pale, pained glimmer. The astral entity held the power.

Discussion

What more can be learned about the astral force of marijuana from these powerful experiences?

In both instances where the clients entered the exercise deeply, they experienced the craving from a different perspective, making direct comparison more difficult. In the first, the craving force or entity was seen and experienced directly, whereas in the second case the focus was on the client's relationship to the craving from the position of receiver. Despite this, strong similarities are present:

- In both instances explored, the clients were surprised and shocked by the evil, almost predatory force of the craving—so different from their previous descriptions—a wolf in sheep's clothing. The illusion that dope was a friend was shattered.
- Each of them encountered an astral entity—one a beast-like clawed arm that hooked into her and the other, a "humanoid" character, described as having charcoal-grey, bark-like large, strong arms and hands—strong similarities in character. They were both tiny in relation to the size of these beastly forces. Each experienced extreme helplessness in the face of the entity.
- In one instance, there was a prelude of gentle enticement, and this could well have been related to the needs the dope came to fill. She used as an entry point an example of a time she was feeling quite good. She did mention that sometimes the craving also came in as a shock—raw, a jolt, pushing her (similar to the first client).
- They were reduced to a pained, helpless state when the craving force (astral entity) attacked and entered them. Each encountered an extremely painful, repetitive emotional state they wished to avoid. The inviter/receiver was a pained and reduced part of themselves as distinct from their full adult self. The illusion that they in their adult presence chose to smoke was also shattered.
- Each experienced the force as further sapping and depleting their strength. The beast appeared to have investment in increasing their demise and their need for the relief the drug promised. Their need gives him power, keeps him alive.

- The entity in both instances appeared suddenly, shockingly, organically, as the client tapped into the needy one.
- In both clients the entity took away love with destructive criticism, not allowing their true self/voice to be expressed.
- The astral entity seemed to be attached to unresolved, painful dynamics in these clients, as both later owned the dynamics and dealt with them.

What is the Astral Entity of Marijuana and What Is its Appearance across Clients?

Here are two examples of the phenomena of the clients' experiences of their inner reality, showing considerable internal consistency. A bigger sample would need to be studied to draw conclusions about the replicability and consistency of this astral parasite. Whether it has characteristically different appearance/behavior from the parasite of other addictive substances is outside the realm of this chapter. However, the writer suspects this could be the case, based on some experience with other addictive substances. For example, one client with a heroin addiction reported how it affected his thinking and feelings, as: detached, clear thinking, and absence of feeling, as distinct from the effects of marijuana (see next section), and based on the fact that this is substantiated in the literature. For instance, feeling closed off to feeling and to others, being "all head" and having no fear, as the effects of heroin,[3] and others refer to the effects of heroin as increasing metabolism and will activity.[4] As the effects are different, perhaps the character of the craving parasite is also different. This needs further investigation.

What Impact Did Discovering the Character of this Astral Entity Have on Clients?

We will address this question with an awareness of Rudolf Steiner's conception of the fourfold human being. In summary, the effects of exposing and confronting the "beast" of the craving belong primarily

3 Dunselman (1993:148–150).

4 Vogt (nd).

in bringing consciousness into the clients' astral realm or soul (containing thinking, feeling and willing functions), although the self (spiritual) was also strengthened as a result of the clients' response and subsequent work. Changing their response in the session, from defending against pain and fear to confronting it, would also have impacted their etheric body, where habits are held. Repercussions were actually *felt* in the etheric for the second client. Dramatically changing the clients' perceptions and shattering their illusions (just outlined) served to promote the healing process in a number of ways:

- Through exposing the phenomena, their wisdom was made visible (in thinking).
- The feeling realm was also impacted, beginning with the shock and horror experienced initially—so different from the warm, fuzzy feelings they associated with the drug. As all Psychophonetics work on addictions influences this realm, the writer chose to concentrate on those effects more specific to this experience.
- It served to increase their will to change their relationship to the dope—both through their awareness of their will being split, the release of will forces held in the entity, and from confronting and defeating its power.

It is generally recognized that the self, as a psychological-spiritual construct, is given over to the substance used in addictions.[5] That the user's will is split is a more particular concept recognized in the way Psychophonetics understands addictions.[6]

Both clients were exposed to their direct experience of the loss of their true self and the appearance and will of the craving. It exposed their illusions that they chose the substance, it was their friend, and that they were more connected to themselves, others, and the universe—it was not them, but the consciousness-changing substance. Furthermore, this realization increased both their intention and desire to reclaim their strength—they each changed their wish to regain their strength and

5 Bloch and Singh (1995); Dunselman (1993).

6 Tagar (1998a).

they mustered the strength of their own creative, spiritual forces in the process—all these processes can be seen as will-strengthening activities. Will, though primarily a soul activity, exists in seven different forms in different realms of the human being: as decision, intention and wish in the thinking; as desire and motivation in the soul; as drives, habit and action in the etheric body; and as instinct in the physical body.[7] Will forces in thinking, the astral and the etheric were engaged and strengthened by exposing, confronting and reclaiming personal power in relation to the force. Moreover, in the writer's opinion, working with the astral entity is particularly important for marijuana users, because their will forces are weakened more by the drug's effects, both short- and long-term. These effects are widely recognized in mainstream thought and literature.

A richer understanding can be gained from the anthroposophic perspective in that when the self leaves during the dope experience, the astral body is lifted up, contributing both to the feelings of relaxation and leaving troubled thoughts and feelings behind.[8] Also, the etheric body is loosened, making for the heavy, lazy, stoned sensation. The willing force in the astral body has difficulty connecting with the physical body to carry out tasks, hence purposeful behavior is reduced. This is coupled with the drug's direct effects on the brain (due to THC, the drug's psychoactive isomers) reducing consciousness, inducing dreaminess and loss of concentration—the user increasingly loses any will. From another perspective, Jost Sauer,[9] whose phenomenological base uses traditional Chinese medicine, gives reasons for lack of will in dope smoking. He sees marijuana as entering via the liver (as the seat of action and direction), reducing liver yang and chi forces, before it travels to the heart (affecting feelings and emotions).

---

7 Tagar, 1998; and Steiner (1996).

8 Dunselman (1993).

9 Jost Sauer (2006).

Reflecting on All Clients

In reflecting on working with these four clients as a whole, this writer was aware of depleted will in many forms, as wavering commitment to recovery, both within and between sessions, with evasions, resistance, cancellations, homework not followed up despite great enthusiasm at the time. A contributing factor may be that the opportunity to participate in a research on the recovery from addiction was offered; they did not have to summon their will to initiate working with a counselor on this issue. However, enabling them to make and maintain a continuing commitment became a major challenge for the counselor. There was a lot of internal bargaining observable and cited by the clients. There was one other client who appeared very interested in the work offered and, after many conversations, put it off, saying it was important to him, but he would probably wait until after Christmas. This could usefully be perceived in the context of reduced and wavering will forces. Hence, this confrontation presented by the astral parasite became a particularly important will-strengthening opportunity, which significantly increased each client's overall commitment to recovery from addiction.

Each client was able to connect with spiritual forces themselves, independently of the drug, to invoke a character to counteract the power of the craving force, and to own those qualities in themselves. Again, this process seems to be particularly important for dope smokers, many of whom cite the pleasure of connecting with spirit and feeling fullness, rather than aloneness/alienation, as high on their list of benefits of the drug (see table 2, page 212). Although many workers in the general addictions field may see spiritual connection as a reason for drug use, users rarely cite it consciously. The dissolving, uplifting effect of dope makes this cosmic connection more available than with other drugs.

In many areas of this work, for example, Narcotics Anonymous, addicts are encouraged to surrender to a larger power of external spiritual guidance. A major strength of the Psychophonetics work is in empowering clients to connect with and own their own inner guidance, as well as be able to connect with a higher power.

They were able through these actions to strengthen the self—to stand more fully present. Again, this is common to any other addictions work, but appears particularly important in view of the previous illusions around self. Each chose different methods to overcome the power of their beast: *Client 2* confronted and invoked spiritual strength, as a process of going beyond an inner threshold. From that position, she offered him love, thus taming the "beast" within; and *Client 4* Resourced, attending to her inner child's needs earlier, in the process of overcoming reactions. She invoked spiritual resources: *the wise woman,* to protect and guide her in her life.

Each changed the pattern of avoidance and suppression within themselves, bringing their own strength to bear. This was personal development work, of taking responsibility for their emotions and processing them, on a path of personal evolution.

In the follow-up review, each client attributed great importance to confronting the astral entity. For both, it was very powerful; in one case, equal to, and in the other, marginally less important than discovering a wise, knowing part within that gave them the knowledge and confidence they sought to make their place and mark in the world. This served to replace a "hole" each had felt without the drug. Both clients were able to ground their spirituality in their own being. Understanding their life motives and the spiritual dimension are two of the four most common motives for smoking marijuana,[10] supporting their desire as being quite typical and showing the importance of this healing work.

The work of Susan Morrison, a senior Psychophonetics counselor specializing in drug rehabilitation also supports the clients' reports. She cites the process she calls "Visioning"—of putting something new into place, inviting a better life through learning how to bring spirit into one's inner life, as inspiration that fires their imagination, as the unique contribution that Psychophonetics makes to the recovery process.

---

10 Felicitas Vogt (table 2, Summary of Findings," pages 212–213).

For Client One, confronting the astral force came in the first session, which was enough for her to stop smoking for two months after using almost daily. She reported a deep difference to her body that she described as cellular, and almost no craving. This can be seen as change in her etheric body.

The astral entity provided yet another personal development opportunity as, interestingly, both these clients went on later to own the destructive craving dynamic personified by the craving force, in that they each acknowledged it from their childhood. "IT" became the raw material for them to face, incorporate and heal more of themselves. In the first example, the squashed heart state she experienced from the craving force reemerged in a later session as the force of her mother's expectations that prevented her from expressing her own truth: "It's always with me—not being right or doing the right thing by her." The second client recognized her father's angry voice critically undermining her as described. This begs the question, whose beast is it anyway? As the client takes more responsibility, he/she seems to gain the strength to own the darker or shadow aspects of the self, which perhaps in previously being disowned and denied, welcomed the entrance of the astral force and gave it the substance to feed on. Or alternatively, more simply, the material exposed could be seen as a core underlying need exposed and made available to be healed by one's own efforts, thereby neutralizing the power of the craving.

In view of the above points, perceiving and confronting the craving force in recovery from marijuana addiction appears to be very valuable as part of the recovery process. The special contribution of Psychophonetics methodology allows this force to become visible. Processing and meeting the underlying needs the drug comes to meet is vital as in all addictions, and working with alterations in strength of feelings, and in rebuilding energy and boundaries through lifestyle and nonverbal expression, are also most important.

Conclusion

Although all four clients gave their verbal impressions of the character of the craving force, the astral energy of the craving for marijuana only emerged organically in two of the four clients. There were some differences and many similarities in the character, appearance and effects of this experience, and its place in the context of processing the healing of marijuana addiction. Perceiving and confronting the craving force seems to be particularly valuable with cannabis. The character of the craving changes dramatically with deeper exploration.

Psychophonetics methodology makes a special contribution in allowing material previously unconscious to become visible, serving to expose the illusions that the drug is a friend and that, with it, one has deeper connection with self, others and the environment/cosmos. The client is confronted powerfully with the loss of self and deceptions accompanying these experiences. The client's perception changes dramatically. The split will is exposed, and can serve as a catalyst to work to reclaim one's power in the face of the astral parasite. Inner expression and spirituality can be owned and grounded in one's physical being. Exposing the astral parasite of the craving for marijuana can at most be axiomatic, and at least make a strong contribution to increasing clients' commitment to regain their power over the drug's influence. This confrontation is particularly important with marijuana addiction, given the needs this drug comes to meet and its physical, mental and psychological effects on the individual.

Table 2: Summary of findings

1. Needs that marijuana comes to meet

Client 1 (22 yrs)	Client 2 (29yrs)	Client 3 (42yrs)	Client 4 (45yrs)
- release from boredom - fun & pleasant feelings - release from worry, thinking - feeling smoke in the lungs - freedom from inhibition - feeling loved	- social enhancement (connection) - spiritual connection - excitement & adventure	- release from tension - ease, don't care attitude	- release, relief, relax - connection to the self & surroundings - deep connection with self & others - sense of oneness with a group - sensory, bodily connection - fullness - excitement, original creative thoughts - perception heightened

2. Underlying needs covered by the drug

- release from agitated, disconnected, helpless part of self	- release from wounds & hurts from the past (incl. pre-birth exp. of		- release from irritated, frightened, alone, empty, unheard, loss of

- comfort from fear of abandonment - feeling loved & cared for - connected to others, feeling happy & loved - release from frozen, numb state, no energy - with heart vulnerability	being unloved, unwanted) - 4/5 yr old alone, ignored - 9 yr old, cracked heart-suppressing her truth - teenager unloved by father, not worthy - current self, self judging, anger & disillusionment with mother & self		voice "I'm not good enough" - 6 yr old – fear of getting it wrong, of showing self, panic - protection from inner critic - abandoned baby

3. *Literature*

Felicitas Voigt	**Jost Sauer**
Areas smoking marijuana come to fill	Why do you smoke marijuana?
○ Intense fulfilling relationship to reality	○ Chill out
○ Warmth, well-being, accepted, seeing into the heart of relationships.	○ Feel high
	○ Feel happy
○ Meaningfulness in one's activities, security in understanding one's life motives	○ Be more sociable
	○ Enhance creativity
○ Religious experience – the spiritual dimension of existence	○ Intensify senses
	○ Expand consciousness

Chapter 13

Working with Alcohol and Other Drugs

Psychophonetics Insights and Practice

Susan Morrison

Part One: An Overview

Traditionally Alcohol and Other Drug (AOD) counseling have had particular approaches based on either the twelve-step model or social learning theories. More recently, other therapies have begun to be included as useful in their approaches such as narrative therapy, family therapy, psychodynamic approaches, cognitive behavioral therapy (CBT), rational emotive therapy, art and music. Therapeutic communities are residential AOD facilities that promote a holistic program with the foundation of a "clean and safe" place. Most of these communities have developed from grassroots initiatives and have been under-resourced, though that is changing a little. They are complex and interesting places and have become a life-changing opportunity for many individuals and for people on drug related charges who are diverted from prisons.

My experience of the AOD field has largely been in therapeutic communities in Western Australia, and for the worker/counselor they can be exciting and challenging places. It is difficult to describe the depth of appreciation one arrives at in seeing the importance of long-term holistic development in all aspects of the client's life. A therapeutic community promotes harmony between the inner and outer life, and calls out the "I am" by encouraging the adult self to come into proper relationship with others.

To have an interest in the spiritual or transpersonal approach is not so alien in a field where a higher power is considered important, although this is not the case with all recovery programs. The overall intention is to reestablish balance in a person's life by regular routines for waking, sleeping and eating, thereby facilitating etheric life health in a way that a dependent person cannot do in the broader community. Given this better physical and psychological foundation and the safety of a loving community, an opportunity arises for receptivity to personal growth and healing that is unique.

My perception of the residents after working at a therapeutic community for many years is that ninety-five percent of the residents had experienced severe trauma. This was largely childhood trauma, sometimes adolescent and/or young-adult trauma. They often began using drugs or alcohol in early adolescence as a self-medicating tool. Other factors are clearly part of the picture and relate to constitution, temperament and the individual's soul strength. It has helped me to see a person as a soul with his/her own destiny, as this allows the necessary appreciation, harmlessness and stepping back needed when one is privileged with so much exposure to another's vulnerability. The risk of countertransference is high, especially when working with young adults who present as "childlike."[1]

Psychophonetics and anthroposophic thinking and practice, plus some strong clinical awareness, form the basis of my approach. For example, one can observe the link, or difference between sensitivity/anxiety, and power/intensity in the energetic nature, in the light of ego development. This range of awareness provides insight into neurotic conditions and personality disorders and highlights the deeply pathological nature of some defense mechanisms and the need for release/relief from chronic anxiety.

1 Marsh and Dale (2006).

An understanding of the importance of facing and redeeming the *inner child* was consolidated by experiencing client processes using the tools of Psychophonetics and supported by the theoretical and practical work of the family therapist John Bradshaw and many AOD theorists. Other critical family systems concepts in recovery are attachment and separation issues. As children attempt to separate out from the family, they must rely on healthy or unhealthy patterns of early attachment. Poor esteem arising from various forms of abandonment or abuse is damaged further by the false promises of drug use. This initiates a desperate attempt to meet unmet needs.

After working with exercises based on energetic principles, the idea of "openness and closed-ness" to life began to influence my way of thinking. Any desired repeated experience is an attempt for the person who desires to repeat an experience that held safety, or the comfort space, as some would call it. This places a different spin on the idea of addiction/dependency.

In the anthroposophic fourfold model of the human being, patterns of experience can enter the body and become fixed over time, including thought/feeling patterns or one's focus, creating a picture of the consolidated sentient body, with unconscious, thinking, feeling and somatic drives tied up in certain practices and habits that have become unconscious, or partly unconscious. In the instance of trauma, these false needs are further hooked into deep fears such as the fear of life, the fear of death, and the fear of nothingness.[2] The critical factor appears to be forms of abandonment abuse, which from an energetic point of view are serious ways of not being present to the child, for example, in parental substance dependency.

The dependent person dives inwardly for affirmation and justification rather than face the world. One of the main consequences of dependency therefore is isolation. It takes the forms of the popular selfishness, the sociopathic tendency to care only about oneself, and heightened self-consciousness/paranoia, plus the tendency to think

2 Treichler (1989); see chapter on neurosis.

that ego dramas are real-life dramas. Another consequence is a more personalized and immature personality, which is the natural developmental phase of adolescence, but indicates arrested development for an adult.[3]

This enhanced subjectivity takes the place of one's healthy ability to experience the world and therefore develop in a balanced way. One can imagine the distortion of personality development if the relationship with self, through something like alcohol, begins at twelve years. It is interesting to note that unless you know a person, this type of "closed-ness," whether it be through their well-rehearsed egoistic stories of glory or of victimhood makes it difficult to discern how available they are for a counseling relationship (or any relationship).

How is this balance between self and the world restored? In the book *Rock Bottom*, the importance of the center region of the soul is spoken about, and it describes how the polarity between the body and the intellect can appear extreme in drug "using" individuals. Impediments of an over-developed intellect or feeling disordering are deceptively difficult to address. According to Rudolf Steiner's insights, the attributes of "beauty, play, and artistry" are keys to the development of the center or feeling self, the heart of our soul life and being one's true self. The strength of this central region of soul supports the self in facing life's challenges.[4] Somatic, artistic methods and resourcing that free up the breathing are great allies in this work.

Rudolf Steiner gave preconditions or attitudes to life for personal/spiritual development that can become a guide toward forming correct relationships with the world and others. In the case of drug users, a capacity to think logically and objectively, which should be a developmental modeling from parental adults, cannot be presumed, and moral development based on trust and experiencing love and continuity and therefore healthy attachment also cannot be presumed. An attitude of appreciation of life and of the natural world are necessary for balanced

3 Treichler (1989); see chapter on adolescence.

4 Tagar (1996d).

development; however, for many drug users, this is a foreign idea and an even more foreign experience. Steiner describes the practice of wonder and gratitude, which establishes a sympathetic relationship to the world and draws on spiritual energies that support us. These ideas can support and guide the counselor without any moralism.[5]

In the book *In Place of the Self,* Ron Dunselman[6] postulates that each drug favors a certain soul faculty and, therefore, with continued use that soul faculty dominates. This can be extended to the idea of personality, which is an expression of the soul. One sees certain personality characteristics dominant in users of particular substances. This is nothing new, as everyone knows what too much alcohol does to a person. It often makes the person loud, insensitive, loquacious, egoistic and often hostile. If you meet this sort of personality you may make the assumption that you cannot get through to them, that there is no point in an exchange, as there is a "closed-ness" in the personality, with very little insight into it. Alcohol, being a depressant, is clinically associated with depression, even though it is usually anxiety that it is initially targeting, but as with most drugs, the opposite is achieved longer term. The drinker becomes more anxious and has no nervous strength and emotional resilience without the drug. The very faculty one seeks to strengthen is weakened. Depression and anxiety exist on the same axis, like a vicious circle.

Psychosophy describes the nature of astrality as being volatile like the wind, rising and falling and creating whirlpools in the feeling nature, and in depression, collapsing into the bodily forces like a bubble caught in a mud pool.[7] If the self falls prey to shallow ego processes, holding these emotional forces stable becomes impossible and the inevitable overwhelms and creates another trigger for *using*. Another problem with the nature of astrality, with its sensations, emotions and feelings, is that the allure of experience seduces us with our curiosity, imagination and rationalization, all supporting the experience of a distorted perception.

5 Steiner (1994).

6 Dunselman (1993).

7 Steiner (1999).

In the case of amphetamines, just staying awake and experiencing is a drug in itself. Again, the repeating of these experiences leads to a grandiosity in the personality of the drug user, which consolidates because the reflective reality-check function of the ego is damaged or underdeveloped. Lack of sleep is further debilitating, as the necessary nighttime spiritual processes do not occur, with the threat of destabilization and psychotic break, especially if the person has a constitutional weakness, in which case, the person may be triggered into a more serious mental illness.[8]

In the broader picture of working with dependency, there are these types of schisms with the self and others that are created by continued use of a substance or habit. In getting a sense of this, it is very difficult to discern because individuals can have huge variance in their constitutional and spiritual development. Inner strength of soul and ego development do appear to be the modifying factors, as well as moral development given in formative relationships in the form of love and responsiveness.

We live in a culture that is functionally dependent on many substances and activities. We all allow ourselves to be motivated by external events, desires, and relationships; however, it does appear that the more compulsive the need, the more dysfunctional the relationship to the object/person is. If we see the human tendency to repeat experiences one likes, in order to feel secure, we can see the normal, abnormal and pathological expressions of it. One of the deeper expressions of these closed patterns is that the "user" begins to suffer intense boredom.

When this has been explored through Psychophonetics counseling, what appears at the bottom of boredom is agony. For most people, their vulnerability is triggered by people and relationships, with a deep need revealed for love, acceptance and contact. When this has been denied they experience emptiness, with the consequent agony of a primal failure to fulfill.

---

8 Treichler (1989)—see chapter on mental health.

Going through this deep unraveling of feelings is the gift that Psychophonetics brings, as once the nature of the layers of feelings are revealed, this strengthens the counseling process and offers more possibilities for the client.

In the practical group work, sensual/sentient experience is powerful for addicts as they have so much inherent power in these sentient forces that as therapists, we have to ask: How are the therapist and the individual who is addicted going to compete with this intensity?

These forces are released incorrectly into the conscious mind by hallucinogenic drugs and are forces relating to auditory and image-making processes such as one might experience in a dream.[9] However, while it is an interesting and sometimes horrible pathological experience for the drug user, it can weaken the stability of the psyche and make one more vulnerable to flashbacks and general confusion. For the person suffering mental illness, however, maintaining some sense of stability and making sense of the world is a full-time focus. Working out what is real, what is true, what is true for them, and what is the next course of action, takes huge amounts of energy. Often psychiatric drugs are helpful but they also add another factor to the variables for the person to manage. Unfortunately, in cases of co-morbidity (AOD and mental-health issues), the individual seeks refuge in not having to do the work of regulating the psyche for a period while stoned. Regaining stability becomes more difficult after the lapse away from consistent effort. For the not-so-mentally-ill users, it can slowly lead to a compromise in them, in which they are satisfied with defining themselves in simpler and secure concepts/defenses, for their identity.[10]

The power of the drug experience, in a less pathological sense, is still an experience that is difficult to compete with. I have observed this in Psychophonetics counseling sessions, in that it is more difficult for people to be in touch with their senses, as they tend to live in their mental process, either because of having to become cunning and fearful

---

9 Treichler (1989).

10 Treichler (1989); see chapter on addiction.

to survive, or because the physical receptors to life have become dulled and the somatic center feels empty. In addition, the excarnation/disassociation type processes of escaping reality, which the drug facilitates, become less of a habit and become a more permanent state of being.

Part 2: A Practical Approach

My practical approach to the problem of stolen intensity and motivation comes from Anthroposophy, Psychophonetics and transpersonal psychology in its creative approach to the transpersonal realm. Only the *magic* of life can compete with the intensity of drug use. It has to be met on its own ground, that is, with less conscious but very rewarding experiences. As commonly understood in the anthroposophic approach, maturity and spiritual growth are transformative processes. Spiritual longings that often have no expression in modern life are also factors in the emptiness that drives addiction. One life phase that carries a deficit unfolds into another unknown inability to be fully present in later life.

Psychophonetics, with its theoretical and methodological roots in Anthroposophy, provides a safe methodology for accessing both deeper and higher realms. In using these tools we need to have faith that a human being inherently has the capacity for higher thought and finer feelings. If we are cut off from that, we need to reach out for it again. In the process of knowing ourselves and as a natural development of sensing into sensation and feelings, the creative use of imagination in the therapeutic process heightens and deepens the perception of the self. Through this we are guided to reach for more spiritual qualities or openness to life, which have been forgotten or not aspired to previously.

Encouraging the development of imagination is a strong part of the Psychophonetics work. Learning to connect with their own inner soul life rather than seek an external substance that has a huge cost attached, raises people's curiosity. Tools such as journaling, creative writing, creative visualizations, dramatizing and various artistic exercises can be tailored to suit the needs and strengths of the individual.

Group work within the therapeutic community originally began as a review process for clients in their recovery, with such questions as: What have I achieved? What are the indicators of such achievement, and how can I hold onto that? The creative and artistic work in these sessions, though based on cognitive understandings from the solid work of AOD programs (the experiential and creative work), play an additional important role in the recovery process.

Problems associated with dependency are as many as the persons involved; however, some fall into more common areas. These include secondary addictions, poor esteem, arrogance, despair, depression, chronic anxiety, anger, both passive and aggressive, perfectionism, grief, loss, obsessive thinking, fears and unmet needs. Knowing the issues involved, I developed a model that could contextualize the recovery process called "The Heart's Journey." This idea is based loosely on Robert Johnson's idea of the journeys of the Hero and Heroine. Group topics are divided into three types based on "clearing," "centering," and "visioning." Issues have to be cleared in the process of learning to become more empowered within or connected with inner resources, and consolidated with the ability to strengthen our center. Later on, we need ways of thinking and a vision for a different way of being, even if it is just envisioning another way of speaking. Overall, the client's joy and expectations of themselves and their life are raised by the inspiration of creative personal work. The following is a description of this program.

The Heart's Journey

Purpose—The groups are based on the idea that recovery from addiction is similar to recovery from a life crisis, as there is so much loss and rebuilding to do. These groups attempt to bring a deeper, creative, experiential level to the client's personal work, to inspire confidence in client's to work with their feelings and energies in a "drug free" way. The overview gives the group an image of a bridge they are building inwardly, across the chasm of addictive patterns and experiences. There are three categories of groups:

1. *Groups on clearing*—letting go of or processing emotional pain
2. *Groups on finding and strengthening their center*—finding identity based on heart powers of conscience and courage
3. *Groups on visioning*—learning skills to create meaning through imaginative thinking.

Samples Topics of Group Work

Clearing—Exploring and clearing feelings using art, understanding dependency needs and attachments, understanding vulnerability, understanding feelings

Centering—Developing self-compassion; identity, self-actualization and adult needs; creating affirmations; intimacy with self and others—consolidating authenticity

Visioning—Focus and mental strength, symbols of self-transformation, creative journaling, creative writing.

Content

Most classes involve a model or idea to challenge or interest people, and to create group discussion, plus an experiential and imaginative element based on their inner work. Experiential work included, depending on the session: warming up, sensing, dramatizing, artwork, and the opportunity to support others.

An example of a series of groups: A series of groups at the third level of education might consist of twelve to fourteen groups, taken from previous groups and depending on the needs of the client group. Topics include mental strength; preparation for meditation; relationship to thinking—dealing with obsessive thoughts; maintaining personal space; the heart's journey—overview; affirmations; authenticity; objectivity; writing exercise; resistance to self-expression; intimacy—with self; poetry and story writing—using issues arising in the group, and using improvisation to build story into a play for our variety show.

In this work, the importance of each person's personal life story is seen as valuable, creative and exciting. Even the basic tool of using resourcing to connect with a feeling that belongs within them and not to the experience they associate it with, is an amazing discovery. In working with an approach that sees the self as central, the overall guideline and goal is compassion, which means that at any point on our journey, it is not only what is in our psychic space/heart, but our attitude to it that matters.

From this point, I explored characterizations of rarely visible aspects of the personality that we carry around and that exist often as mood states that others can see. I also began working with monologues about difficult experiences; however, this process is not for the faint of heart when working with drug users. Writing, exposing, expressing and dramatizing these memories, moods or qualities serve to value them for the storyteller and recaptures the energy tied up in these experiences that can then become available for the person. The power of language itself serves to connect soul to self in the dramatizing and witnessing.

Larger Groups (up to 20 people)—Drama/Expression Therapy

The larger groups were put together in a slightly different way with a different intention—to be more experiential in a physical way to let go of repressed tension, which is very important with this type of client group. Then, through ideas, sounds and gestures, to challenge their preconceptions in a fun way. These were typical Psychophonetics warm-up group activities tailored to meet the needs of the therapeutic community, then followed by specific dramatic exercises. Examples of these topics are intimidation/assertiveness, ego, gossip, boundaries, personal power, boredom, the adult child.

A Special Purpose Small Group—Anger

This group was specifically put together to encourage residents to explore their anger rather than manage it. Participation was voluntary and I did not accept people until they had been in the overall program for over six weeks. The *intention* is to be exposed to the dynamics of anger, to vicariously and/or explore their own anger with the help of the group. The group provides an energetic container that is strong enough to invoke loud sounds, humor, play and emotional support. The participants support each other in the gestures of exploding held-in tensions, of becoming powerful characters, and in connecting with inner resources. Many participants were men who had issues with anger for many years and had been in and out of prison. The men loved doing this work and showed sensitivity, great humor and insight.

A Case Study: Johnny

In this series of sessions we see a young man, suffering with severe alcohol dependency, typically sensitive and particularly sensitive to judgment in adolescence, and take a journey through his fears, thoughts, and dysfunctional agendas. Johnny is a fine, creative and spiritual thirty-five-year-old man, who presents in the therapeutic community as chronically self-conscious, hunched over in group, not speaking unless spoken to, and then the soul of discretion. He is a gifted individual who could do calisthenics, write poetry, sculpt, sing, and cook. We did a lot more work than these sessions indicate and Johnny is very receptive to working in a creative way. Clinically, he might be seen as extremely neurotic, having created an entirely false self to survive in the world, with a lonely and isolated position inside.

Session 1: Johnny presents in reasonably good spirits today. He had a conflict with another resident this morning, which left him feeling angry. However, the yoga class shifted the anger and he is very pleased with that. We go on to discuss his tendency to obsess and internalize anger. Johnny has doubts about his ability to feel, knows that he is not "sentimental," and questions his ability for any relationship. In his interactions with others, he tends to blame, berate, feel shame, and regret. In this intense questioning process, he agonizes over right and wrong in spiritual and philosophical ways, and finds himself constantly in mental conflict, which he thinks is a hangover from long-term dope smoking. In questioning his ability to feel we discover a few incidents when he knows exactly how he feels.

The emerging dynamic appears to be a process that prevents Johnny from getting close to anyone, as it is all about their needs; he does not reveal or claim his own needs. We talk about his needs and about his many skills, but he could not focus on or claim these things because he constantly dismisses himself to meet others' needs. In this session, he sees the angry obsessing, the self-hate and regrets.

Counseling goals—His goal of finding a direction for the future is to learn self-love, self-care, self-respect, validation and to learn to express his overload of rage and regret, then to express what he needs without feeling ashamed or dismissing those needs. The process is to support him in finding true assertiveness and addressing the gap between his true self, his rage, and what he expresses.

Session 2: Johnny is struggling with the reality of his own deceit, as he has been plotting to smuggle alcohol into the community. We explore this and he says that at age fourteen he became sneaky. He felt his parents' restrictions triggered all forms of rebellion, not just with alcohol. At seventeen years old he was fighting with his parents and wanted to be free. More important, he feels on reflection that this rebellion: "set me against a positive life," and states: "I chose the wrong direction for my cleverness."

The above statement could be a very deep regret. That rebellious "boy" is still looking for attention or approval and he does not think of the consequences. Johnny now feels he has lost direction. He has had huge potential and many skills but is fickle and gets bored easily. Our common picture is Johnny drifting from one person to another trying to make them happy yet arousing suspicion because of giving so much and not needing anything. I ask him to think about a central guiding factor and gave him some questions to think about.

Session 3: Johnny began by speaking about the questions I gave him to think about last week.

Q: I wish I knew what I was frightened of. [his question]
A: I am afraid of failing and of pointlessness.
Q: What is my next step?
A: It feels like a change is happening.
Q: How can I accept my needs and life as a man?
A: It appears that shame is his master. Johnny reflects that he always tries to be good but doesn't understand why he is clinging to deluded morals, that nobody else is that good. During his adolescence, Johnny expressed that he felt ugly, so wanted to be appreciated for his insight, which was highly valued in his family. He also did not want a shallow girlfriend. He is now ashamed of his arrogance, his feelings of superiority and judgment of others.

Expression therapy process (Psychophonetics)—In forming a wish Johnny says: "I want to understand the self-hatred." He enters bodily into the experience of self-loathing and explores it through gesture, finding himself hiding within, as "disappeared" into a cave with bars. There is some safety and feeling of self in this place. He connects with this feeling and is able to feel himself slowly emerging...at least his head and one shoulder can squeeze out of the "cave." Johnny appears elated after this process and completes the session with a process of being grounded and present.

Session 4: Yesterday, Johnny was accepted into the third stage of the program. He was challenged by the community on his self-worth and assertiveness, although his progress in these areas was acknowledged. Today he presents in the session as being positive, feeling more assertive and is getting respect from others. He has changed his victim status in the community and is now speaking in group, although he still shies away from conflict. There is potential through poetry for Johnny to strengthen his inner self and he writes another poem about the "flame"—a spark of joy that is emerging, a soldier of light. In this session we discuss his parents and how he never felt good enough for them because *he nearly excelled but not quite.* Johnny feels that taking care through self-care is becoming more natural and we work on affirmations at this stage.

Session 5: Johnny felt his fear of conflict in group was less intense today. He has been using sculpture and has created a cobra and will now do a warrior. Johnny has ambitions to do stick dancing and fire dancing. Working with his affirmations is helping with self-respect and in his role as WPC (Work Program Coordinator) he now feels respected. Johnny feels he is valuing himself and is thinking more correctly about "people pleasing." Issues were identified to work on in the next session, such as fear of conflict and failure.

Session 6: Johnny is in good health and spirits today. He talks initially about his reflections on drinking. He felt that he would need at least three years with external support, and believes that if he is on his own he will sneak a drink because he got away with it for so long—with seven years of use. He says that he used it to feel sad and grieve/wallow, and it made him feel numb and comfortable. Now he is feeling better and battling the desire to drink and is feeling victorious. As previously identified, the fears he was running away from were fear of conflict and fear of failure. Now he is feeling fear of the future/change/life. Johnny decided to explore his fear of failure. He describes his parents' high expectations and how it works now inasmuch as he expects to achieve his recovery. The trigger that brings on the fear of failure is the idea: "I'm not strong enough," and then he loses confidence.

Expression therapy process (Psychophonetics)—Johnny's wish is: "I would like not to overact to the idea that I could fail." Johnny enters into and explores feelings and gestures, which took him into seeing how at fifteen years old, he was stuck in a void, sitting on the floor in loneliness. In a gesture of despair, he could sense some determination, which he used as a resource to invoke strength against the waves of darkness enveloping him. In this process, using sounds and gestures, Johnny creates a new inner space and energetic boundary. He then returns to dialogue with the inner fifteen-year-old present in the gesture of loneliness and commits to taking ongoing care of him, creating an inner relationship.

Reflections

This selection of sessions is a brief summary of Johnny's process, which includes Psychophonetics counseling and the involvement of the therapeutic community, both of which are integral to his inner work, and demonstrates how the process of peer feedback, earned stature and authority can support the process of recovery. Some further reflections on Johnny's case would include an observation of the nature of repressed needs, the close relationship between authenticity and anger, and how dependent on each other these are for expression. We can see how Johnny's repressed anger in adolescence and his vulnerability to the idea of "goodness" set him up to become a drinker, especially in combination with his gifted intelligence/sensitivity. The conflict between his parents meant that they were not likely to have been focused on his needs and as he strived harder to achieve perfection, it still never got him what he wanted. In adulthood, he continued this pattern of giving and not receiving from anyone who would tolerate him. The role of alcohol served to suppress the real need for connection, which eventually became lost and forgotten, and defensiveness became rigidity of thinking, that is: "this is who I am: a loser!" In Johnny's case, we observe that he is young enough, well enough, and has the inner resources to achieve reintegration and become more present in body and soul.

I would like to add a conclusive note on current AOD practice. Current treatment targets good, supportive habits based on clear thinking and daily programs, which include the understanding of individual and social factors and the nature of the drugs themselves. The focus is on managing stress, anger, emotions, and pharmacotherapies within the broad context of co-morbidity. In working with clients with serious dependency issues, it is important to have solid inner and outer supports in place before they can safely approach trauma counseling.

Chapter 14

An Eco-soul Bush Experience
Therapy in the Bush

Adrian Hanks

Introduction

How can we engage people into a deeper therapeutic process in nature? For many years I have been exploring the application of Psychophonetics in the bush, as a new and exciting way to work with people, which is called: *An Eco-soul Bush Experience: Therapy in the Bush.* Taking Psychophonetics, ecology and nature study, and bringing them all together in this way opens another doorway for working with people in a healthy, positive and nurturing way, to connect to nature, to their soul and to their spirit.

My motivation comes from working with many anthroposophically based initiatives since the mid-1990s, during which time I have become deeply involved with adult education, biodynamics, nature study and observation, and spiritual investigation. Included in the development of this work are many aspects of my experiences, understandings, insights and intuitions, which form these newer ways of working with people on the land and in the open environment of nature. The journey of self-realization and working to explore, heal and transform myself as well as guiding others to do the same, and doing my part to restore and heal the earth, are a big part of my life. I carry a deep longing and passion for being in nature and spend much of my time walking along beaches, in the bush, the mountains or in the desert with my didgeridoo on my back. I make didgeridoos from naturally hollowed timber found in the Australian bush and this has taken me to an even deeper appreciation and understanding of the magical qualities of the didgeridoo. Ritual and ceremony are a big part of my work and life and by connecting to our selves, other people, nature and the spiritual realities through ritual and ceremony, I believe we can begin to reawaken and reconnect to a more holistic way of living. Ritual and ceremony are more alive in some cultures than in others. In some parts of Australia and South Africa, ritual and ceremony are very much alive, owing to the remote areas in which people live, allowing them a deeper and more personal connection to nature.

Therapy in the Bush has become much more defined and refined since working in Byron Bay. Reading about eco-psychology, the name that seems to be most commonly used now in this field of work, has encouraged me to develop this work further and to present it in this chapter. Eco-psychology is a relatively new term for expressing and describing the connection between nature and the psyche, combining the ecological and the psychological. It can be described as follows: "Eco-psychology[1] involves the emerging synthesis of ecology and psychology; the skilful application of ecological insight to the practice of psychotherapy; the study of our emotional bond with the earth; the search for an environmentally based standard of mental health; and redefining *sanity* as if the whole world mattered."

It is certainly not a new way of working and thinking, as there are many old and ancient cultures such as those of the Australian Aborigines and the American Indians that connect psyche and nature. These ways of working with the land, nature, spiritual investigation and the psyche have now been largely forgotten by the western world, but there is a grassroots emergence of eco-psychology work in some areas of healing in the world. *Therapy in the Bush* also falls under the umbrella of eco-psychology.

1 See the definition on the internet: www.ecopsychology.athabascau.ca.

Most therapeutic sessions take place in the confines of a room in a building, devoid of the aspects of nature. By working with clients outside in nature, there is the added advantage of using nature as another healing tool, as a resource, and nature becomes the therapy room or therapy space for reconnecting people to this living world around them.

Psychophonetics is a very effective modality of healing and working in the bush with people who are striving for inner healing and transformation, as the world of nature becomes a mirror of our inner world as well as of the destructive and negative actions and forces we create in the world. Nature becomes a picture of what is happening in our innermost being. We can start to see what needs to be healed inwardly and get a picture of what we might start to implement in our lives to improve our environment, our outer skin. We can match the destruction of our soul to the destruction of the world and learn to restore and heal both.

The poisoned, toxic, polluted, raped, mistreated, uncared for and mismanaged Earth can be a good indicator and reflector of why we are feeling unhealthy, depressed, addicted, angry, frustrated or alienated. A reconnection between soul and soil, soul and nature, and deeper spiritual aspects of life can be found potentially by stepping into a natural environment. Working with aspects of eco-psychology and psychotherapy, the human being can work toward becoming whole again by reconnecting with the wider, deeper, often forgotten aspects of him/her self, which is nature. By stepping into nature, we can begin to see ourselves as part of a greater whole, part of a universal oneness that many of the ancient mysteries describe. This stepping in and reconnecting with nature can bring a richer and more holistic approach to working with the healing process.

Applications

One process includes taking clients into the bush for a whole day, spending about six hours together, exploring and working through the clients' questions and issues in a variety of groupings—with individuals on a one-to-one basis, as a group, or as a workshop. Usually we go to a beautiful place about forty kilometers from Byron Bay called Minyon Falls, which is a National Park, with lots of wildlife and interesting flora. Traveling there by car gives us time to get to know each other and begin to get a picture of what the day may bring. When we arrive at the car park we walk down to a large viewing platform that looks over a waterfall and across a deep rainforest ravine. This is where the deeper inner process begins, right on the edge of the platform; this is where the therapy/coaching/counseling really starts. This is where we make the first choices, the beginnings of a wish to explore, transform and/or heal the issues that we need to work with. This is where the client takes stock of what he/she wants to do during the time we are in the bush.

While standing on this platform high above the trees and rocks below, I ask the participants to use their imagination and to see themselves standing on the viewing platform—like having an eagle's perspective of themselves—and to say what they sense and see going on for them.

This inevitably leads to people going inward and describing what is happening for them in that moment. Often this is a moment when emotions and feelings begin to come up and insights start to be spoken. From this conversation, a common picture is formed among us, while still on the platform. From this, clients decide what it is that they want to work with and they make a wish statement. From then on, the walking journey starts and we set off for our trek into the bush—with the focus on the wish.

When working with people in this way they begin to relate to their inner world in a very profound way through what they see and experience from the abundance that nature has to offer. A connection to an animal, plant or a view across a valley can provoke a feeling within minutes of the session beginning.

Therapy in the Bush with Individual Clients

In one example, a man sees a large goanna (Australian monitor lizard) walking along the bush track, which leads us into a process of what the goanna represents for him and how he sees himself in the goanna. The goanna mirrors for this man what is going on for him in his life. He sees the goanna as a loner, as something/somebody who is not very sociable. The man says that he would like to be more sociable and less "goanna-like," so we look at ways in which he can become more sociable and what it is that stops him from doing so. The connection of being outside in nature sparks something deep within the soul. Many amazing things are witnessed as people journey through their process, sometimes with a small stick, a rock or even the sighting of a goanna. The more this work continues, the more I am aware of the disconnection that people have with nature and also with their own inner world of the soul.

Another client is a smoker and smokes twenty to thirty cigarettes a day. We spend seven hours in the bush together and when she feels the urge for a cigarette, we work together through a process to alleviate and establish some ways to cope with the cravings that are taking place during the day. We do this using visualization and by using the image of a Banksia flower, with which she feels a connection. The flower represents for her the person that she wants to become, and that person is not a smoker—the image of the flower reminds her about her choice of not smoking.

She enters a process of sensing and gesturing what is happening as the craving arises and creates a picture/feeling of what is going on inside her belly. She describes a blackness and the feeling of it and then transforms that with a new color imagination of yellow, the color of the Banksia flower. She does this throughout the day and it keeps the cravings at bay. She'd had only one cigarette all day while in the bush, and that was immediately after lunch.

Follow-up: Several days after the eco-soul bush experience, this client calls to say that her cigarette smoking had reduced dramatically and she feels it is now time to stop completely. She says that she has bought a painting of Banksia flowers and it is hanging in her living room to remind her of who she wants to become. The fresh air and natural surroundings of nature certainly helped with the smoking issue. The following is an excerpt from a letter that this client wrote following her experience in the bush:

> After years of corporate training on how to communicate I arrived at Byron Bay to see Adrian with the hope that maybe he could "crack me." I had my doubts. I had years of hiding my true self. I had seen many psychologists and counselors, had years of company training, and read numerous books on how to appear confident and handle my emotions. I had spent all of my life living someone else's dream, covering my true emotions, too scared to leave as I didn't know who I was or what I wanted to do. Uncovering the layers of defense I had so successfully built over the years...It was extremely moving, empowering, a life-changing experience. I found my heart space and left knowing and understanding myself a lot better. An increase in self-love and self-respect, I found my centre and a connection with my soul.

By supporting people to reconnect to nature and to their inner world of soul, they can begin to work through deep-seated issues and questions and become able to bring them into the outer world, into a space that is shared in the bush. We share many moments of conversation, movement, tears, joy and deep understanding, with the support of the natural surroundings to hold us in these spaces. Something happens in the realms of nature that is very freeing and cannot be found fully in an enclosed space in a building. It seems that we are naturally reconnected to more of our whole being when in nature. The space that nature provides reconnects us to the greater whole, to a more complete picture of who we are as spiritual beings. Reconnecting with this feeling of being a spiritual being in nature, in the world, in the universe, is a profound experience for many people. Moments of a new awakening are frequent for many clients and days or weeks afterward, clients report that their lives have changed in amazing ways as a result of their sessions in the bush.

Therapy in the Bush with a Group

A group of people were taken into a beautiful arboretum outside of Cape Town, in South Africa, in the early spring of 2004. We spent some time adjusting to our new surroundings, our new environment, to our new skin. Each person is asked to go and find a tree to connect to and to spend some time with it, to begin some sort of dialogue with the tree and to get a picture of who and what the tree is for them. After this, we gather again to share the experiences within the group.

The first person to share his experience describes in great detail how he experienced the emotional state of his chosen tree, the way it expresses itself through its shape, how it speaks and how it feels being in the arboretum. The tree is a mirror for him, and he is expressing his inner world with the tree being a mirror of his inner soul.

Another person introduces us to her experience of a tree. She had been sitting next to the trunk of a tree and gone into a meditation. She had an inner visual experience of running across an open plain, hunting with others and holding a spear in her hand. There was a group of hunters and she was part of it. She goes on to describe the scene in great detail. It is a very powerful picture of a tribal African hunt. When she finishes sharing her experience, she says that she is not feeling very happy as she had enjoyed being the powerful and courageous hunter and now she is feeling weak and powerless. Her wish is "to be powerful and courageous in her life now."

The client's wish gives the counselor and the client a direction for action. We discuss how to proceed, and we go to a small clearing to draw a large circle about four meters in diameter in the soft leaf-covered earth. Then we each pick up a thick stick just over a meter long and step into the circle. For the next ten minutes, we do not go out of the circle as we engage in a mock battle. The rest of the group sit outside the circle as witnesses. We move around in the circle until near the end of the time when she says that she feels like a warrior queen and expresses another wish: "to be a warrior queen." She then tells the group how she needs to become more like a warrior in her life, to deal with all the stuff she has to deal with. Then she goes for a walk by herself to really feel and deepen this connection with the *warrior queen* quality.

While she is gone, the rest of the group start to make a crown for her from leaves, twine, bark and grasses. We also find a log for a throne, wood for a scepter and mace, and we create a special area that is fit for a queen's coronation. When she returns she is asked if she can honor herself, and whether she has the strength to carry the queen quality inside. She says that she can and is feeling strong and queen-like. We rake back a big mound of leaves and she lies down on the earth. We cover her with the leaves and she lies there for several minutes. When she is ready, she rises out of the leaves and walks into the space we had created for her. There she is adorned with the crown, the scepter and the mace. Together we create a sacred and personal ritual.

Follow-up: A few weeks later, she reports that this day has been one of the biggest turning points in her life. She went to her father's house shortly afterward and healed some old wounds with him, which had been there for many years. She also had the courage to end a relationship that had previously been difficult to end.

Another group member is walking along a track near where she had her tree experience and became aware of a "samurai warrior" shape appearing in a treetop. She points him out and we can all see the shape and face of him on the tip of the tree. I invite her to enter into a dialogue with him and she tells us that he was a stuck samurai spirit who was fed up with fighting, fed up with the role he had to carry. He did not want to fight anymore. I ask her if there is any way in which she can help him. She says she can teach him the way of the "empty hand." She can show him a way in which he no longer has to use his samurai sword or fight anymore. She demonstrates to us a beautiful karate *kata*. In this ritual, she frees up an aspect of herself, of feeling years of being in bondage to a certain role. It is a deep and powerful process in the middle of the forest.

As we are leaving the arboretum in the late afternoon we come across a stone medicine or healing circle under some trees, so we finish our day in the forest with a meditation and an honoring of our journeys.

There are many mysteries in the world and when we are in nature, we can begin to see and work with some of them. The time in the forest was certainly a day of mystery, intrigue and healing. Working with the support of nature as a tool in therapy, can make the process of healing more holistic, giving more freedom for the use of movement, exploration and sounds. In my experience, clients can feel freer when in the realm of nature, as it can appear less restrictive for them, rather than being confined in a therapy room. However, we must keep in mind that the clients may not be accustomed to being out in nature and it may take some time for them to embrace and adjust to this environment. For some people, if they are not used to being out in nature, this may be a fearful experience.

Without the use of nature in the therapeutic process, are we missing something? Are we missing or ignoring the fact that the unhealthy environment we live in is often a major factor in regard to the connection of our psychological and physiological problems? I believe that by including nature in the therapeutic process we can start to link these factors and connections. Our diet, food, drinks, homes, spaces, rivers, seas, land and air are often out of balance and in need of repair, just like us. When we take these environmental issues into the therapeutic process as major or minor causes of imbalances, maybe we will get a deeper, more developed picture and a deeper understanding of people's psychological and physiological problems.

Therapy in the Bush: Workshop

In the workshops, the aim is to develop or un-develop a picture of the macrocosmic and microcosmic polarities by bringing in a meditation to build a connection with the outer universe, the earth and the group members together. Carrying thoughts and beliefs, such as we are separate, less than, or better than, can keep us cut off from our spirituality.

A simple exercise is to pull a small plant from the soil and see it wither before your eyes. We can see the connection of the plant and the soil straight away, and this can be taken deeper and deeper into what other connections there are. When working with people it is sometimes not quite so easy for them to see their disconnectedness with the planet, their environment, or themselves.

A Short Exercise to Begin a Workshop

Feel your feet connected to the earth just like the roots of a plant. Feel the weight of your being standing on the earth. Feel your full weight bearing downward. Now slowly, try levitating, letting go of the connection, being free of the earth. Even though our mind, soul or spirit may soar, our bodies do not. We are bound to the earth, connected.

In the biodynamic/nature workshops, we take the group into nature and ask participants to sit or stand for about fifteen minutes, taking in all that they experience around them. After this, we share our experiences and then close our eyes to imagine that there is more.

Being in the same spot again, the instruction is now to sit with their attention on themselves—on their breathing, heartbeat and their connection to the ground. In this experience, we begin to see that although many new things are experienced during the first part of the exercise, it did not include them, as they were the observers. During the second part of the exercise, they become aware of themselves sitting on the earth, breathing the air, being the observers, being part of the whole experience.

Workshop Experiences

In one workshop situated on a biodynamic farm in Stellenbosch, just outside Cape Town, a woman in her fifties is in tears after experiencing again, after more than forty years, that there are elemental beings around her. As a child, she had been told to stop daydreaming and was discouraged from such experiences. I ask her what that had been like and she describes how she has been feeling "cut off" for all these years. Her wish is "to be able to reconnect again to the elemental beings," but the dampening experiences of her childhood stop her. I ask her to show us what it was like to be "cut off" and she demonstrates this by sitting away from the group. This awareness now gives her a new direction in which she wishes to reconnect and open the doorway for a new perspective, a new way of seeing things.

In these workshops the connection between the soul and nature can be discovered and seen in many of the exercises. This soul/psychotherapeutic work is incorporated into the biodynamic workshops, thus giving biodynamics an even deeper soul-spirit connection. Movement, sound, meditation, visualization, sensing and artistic expression through clay, drawing and poetry are all part of the biodynamic and nature-study workshops. In this way, people are encouraged to see nature from different perspectives.

In another workshop conducted in a small town in KwaZulu-Natal near the Drakensberg Mountains in 2004, there is some discussion about the eucalyptus gum trees and how they are aliens, invaders and how they drink too much water and deplete the water tables under the ground. I listen for a while and then ask the group of about twelve people to walk over to a patch of land that has a big gum tree in it. There are a few smaller trees around but the gum tree is the most commanding by far.

We walk to the center of the clearing where there is a quite dry area. The patch of land is not being shaded by the trees and there are some dry grasses over it. I ask the group to dig into the dry dirt with their hands. They dig down several inches and experience the dry, hard, almost lifeless soil. Then I take them under the gum tree, about six feet from its trunk, to repeat the process. This time they dig into moist soil, which is teeming with life. Their enjoyment and surprise is wonderful to see, and there is an instant change of attitude with a new respect for this "alien" gum tree. We then discuss the benefits of having the gum tree in Africa.

Without some measures being put into place, the eucalyptus trees and the acacia wattle trees do cover the land very quickly. They are just doing the job of shading the soil from the hot sun and dry winds. We can also question why they are there in the first place and why there is so little native vegetation growing in much of Africa. We just see nature from one perspective much of the time, such as seeing the gum trees as invaders, intruders or aliens. I wonder what aspect of our selves these thoughts and beliefs stem from.

In another workshop, one man experiences getting a sore throat from inhaling the perfume of a particular plant. Through movement and gesture, he shows the experience of the energy of the plant and perfume and where and how it is lodged in his throat by moving/gesturing with his hands. When he gestures the experience of the soreness again he says it needs soothing. With his hands he moves what the quality of soothing is like and with the soothing sounds of *"LLLLLLL MMMMMMM"* he moves his hands around his throat. He continues this for a minute or so and then declares that the soreness has gone. This shows how effective it can be when we work with nature and the tools of imagination, visualization and sounds.

Through these exercises, we can begin to reconnect to the realms of nature and begin to use the natural world as a mirror for our own souls. When the natural world speaks to us, can we hear it? We must begin to develop new capacities of knowing and understanding to see and hear the natural world in/around us if we want to connect more wholly to our environment and to our core being. Through reconnecting to nature and her living forces, we can begin to understand and know these inner soul forces on a deeper and more conscious level. To fully engage and connect with the natural world of nature, to feel and understand what we are doing to her and to ourselves, we have to allow our souls to be a mirror, and to become it for a moment. To understand and truly empathize with nature we need to be it.

By finding practical experiences we have the possibility of beginning to find new and imaginative ways of seeing nature. Our whole environment can be seen from another perspective, from another level of consciousness, if we are in nature and observe what is happening there.

In this work, the aim is to facilitate people finding some connection through expression, by finding the creative spark within through poetry, drawing, sculpture, meditation, observation, movement, dance, drama, or even from creating ritual and ceremony. For many people these exercises are new, and planning may need to include time to adjust to the environment. In many of the workshops, there have been strong and deep emotions displayed, with creativity being opened up, allowing connections with deeper realms of nature, such as acknowledging and working with the elemental beings that surround and envelop nature. In this work, I am only, as always, on a journey. Nothing is complete and as this work is unfolding, it is changing, developing, maturing, and challenging, as all good work should, bringing more questions and issues to explore in the bush.

Chapter 15

Darcy's Journey out of Depression
A Case Study

Merri Hughes

The sessions in this case study constitued a remarkable journey for both practitioner and client. The client, Darcy (not her real name), has contributed her own comments and poetry that emerged during the course of attending psychotherapy, which helped to facilitate her journey out of depression.

Session 1: Empathic Connection

Darcy, a forty-three-year-old woman, has been feeling depressed and anxious over the past ten years. While she had actively worked at home in conscious parenting of her six-year-old daughter, and in domestic tasks, Darcy has not been able to engage in paid employment for ten years, and would like to reintegrate back into the local community. In support of this reintegration, Darcy started a writing course and integration aide training, but is worried that her feelings of depression will affect her ability to complete these courses.

Developing rapport with empathic responses and gentle probing facilitated and supported Darcy to discuss a number of deep and intimate issues. Ten years ago, when she was thirty-three years old, Darcy's youngest brother, who was diagnosed with schizophrenia, killed her mother. Eighteen months later, her second-youngest brother killed himself. Darcy now feels it is time to address some of the underlying issues in her depression, disclosing that she often feels fearful and worried that something bad will happen. She fears that one day, if her brother is released from prison, he will kill her, her partner or her child.

Darcy explains how she has difficulties in creating boundaries with people, in knowing which boundaries are okay and which are limiting. She heartfully shares how her brother killed her mother at a time when Darcy had decided to withdraw some high-level support from him, as her own self-care was suffering. During the session, there were periods when Darcy was just being in feeling and sitting in this deeply empathic space, which helps to invite the further unfolding of her story.

She expresses feeling very fatigued, irritated and frustrated over her difficulties in saying what she needs in the face of conflict and aggression, and discloses a history of exposure to violence from the brother who has schizophrenia. By expressing the sense of being blocked in her speaking at these times, she identifies how she feels wounded and in pain. By allowing this blocked feeling to be present, she exposes a deeper layer, in which she keeps sabotaging her own healing, that is, feeling fearful results in her placing restrictions on how she lives life. The more restrictions there are the more she is unable to live life the way she wants to and the more wounded and stuck she feels.

Darcy comments, "I was ready to release the fatigue and limiting effects of these conditions (depression and anxiety) as I had taken positive steps into extending myself back into the community via study, writing and integration aide training. However, irritation, fatigue, and anxiety were increasing, and I did not want not to move forward because of the limiting forces of depression. I was ready to take the next step to understand and be free of depression and anxiety."

This leads into a common picture that there is a paradox, a catch-22, of wanting to express her essential self in the world, yet the feeling of being wounded is running the show, playing out in ways that don't serve her anymore. Darcy's wish toward changing this dynamic became: "To take care of the wounded one." In plotting toward the action phase of the session, I took into account that Darcy was feeling exposed, which suggests a need to develop a sense of protection.

Action phase—Based on her wish as my guide, Darcy senses the presence of this wounded one in her body, and when she feels this connection, she asks, "What do you need?" She listens and finds care and protection are needed. Through a process of first imagining these qualities, Darcy offers care and protection, using movement, color and sound, until she feels this inner need is being fulfilled and she can breathe more easily, and is feeling more in touch and present in her inner life. This completed the first session, and after a short discussion, Darcy agrees that during the following week, she will practice this new way of inner resourcing by spending time listening to what she needs, and to maintain this connection with the qualities of care and protection.

Reflecting on the Session

This was a very moving session with much deep personal content shared. Darcy had not spoken about these issues for a long time and had never been to counseling before. Deep empathy involved holding a space for Darcy's vulnerability and offering heartfelt compassion. Darcy was thirty-three years old when her mother was killed, which from an anthroposophic and biographical perspective can be related to experiences of death and resurrection or rebirth.[1] Darcy is forty-two years old at the time she commences counseling, an age often characterized by significant transformation and spiritual awareness.[2]

Session 2: Earth-Magic Wilderness Woman

Since the last session, Darcy sees more clearly how she sabotages herself through fear and depression, but shares that she has been feeling frustrated and agitated, because she wants to be fulfilling her heart's longing, to write and reenter the workforce. Through an exploration of

1 Burkhard (1997).

2 See Burkhard (1997: 94 & 96–97).

this, Darcy states that during the week she felt the presence of feeling wounded and has been exploring this relationship through the writing course. In our conversation, a deeper layer of feeling reveals to Darcy a new insight that she feels trapped in life, as if she is "tethered." She is not sure what she is "tethered" to, but feels it as heaviness in the body. Our common picture became *a goat tethered on a chain and having to carry the extra weight of the chain, constrained.* This motivates Darcy to make a wish: "I want to feel free of the tethering and heavy weight."

Action phase—Darcy recalls a recent life example of when she felt "tethered." This occurred in a parent action group, in which she was "feeling others are dependent on me." She senses this experience of being tethered in her body and reports feeling pain in her shoulder blades, saying it feels like she is being clawed by some big, black, mythical beast. Darcy gestures this with her whole body, becoming the "beast" and then exits from this position. In beholding this experience, Darcy says:

> This beast flies in the sky and swoops with claws outstretched, piercing my wounded self in one graceful action, enveloping and then engorging and devouring me. As a shape shifter might do, I become this beast and could feel how disconnected it was from my wounded self, I am just prey, I feel compassion for the beast and know that it cannot help itself as it is just hungry.

Darcy then enters, exits, and beholds (EEB) this experience for a second time, and in beholding, she calls the beast the "dragon," which scavenges for food. She says, "My wounded self is tethered to this beast and has been devoured many times before. The claws are always in my back and many dreams have me pinned, unable to move. To be now brave enough to see it materializing in front of my eyes and to enter into it gives me such empowerment. I am on my way and will be free."

To explore deeper, she enters in gesture for a third time, becoming the "Dragon." When Darcy exits and beholds, she describes how the dragon feeds off the wounded self, the one in absolute pain, scared, sad, and depressed, the one that has been devoured many times before. In beholding this, Darcy feels compassion for the dragon and understands that it cannot help itself. She feels this compassion strongly, much more strongly than she does her fear of it. She doesn't wish for it to go away, and says, "In a strange way I feel that the dragon wants to help me but doesn't know how, so keeps devouring the wounded one."

Darcy enters the wounded self, becoming the one being devoured by the dragon. After exiting and in beholding she says, "The wounded self is my joyous self, my wishes, my dreams and my light. As soon as my joyous self begins to be nourished, the dragon devours the wounded self again, as it feeds on light and my confidence and will wane." Darcy enters again and sees a fiery-eyed demon, which appears to have a demonic energy. In exiting and beholding, Darcy says the dragon is trying to protect her from the demon, that the dragon is tethered to the demon:

> What is the beast's name? The darkness? Is it death? The empty void of space that is our life's end? A black hole in space? I know I felt this when my mother died. What is the wounded one's name? Who are these two parts tethered to each other, one through fear, the other hunger? I believe that the beast is a dragon...a mythical battle is being played out within me.

Then the quality and gesture that comes up for Darcy as a natural guard and protection in face of the demon is identified, and she invokes Mother Earth, motherhood, and her own mother, naming this as "earth magic wilderness woman." She fully embodies her in gesture, feeling great strength and courage. In this drama of inner soul characters, the "earth magic wilderness woman" stands between the dragon and the demon and tells the demon to release the dragon, and tells the demon that the power play is to be played out with herself, as: "earth magic wilderness woman." She holds a long stare with the demon, standing looking at it, holding her power, and yells, "Fuck off." In doing this action, she takes on the power of wilderness woman who casts off the darkness of the demon, which has diminished to a speck, thus losing power in her psyche. Darcy says the demon represented fear and depression, and she no longer felt tethered to it, but is finally feeling relieved and free. Darcy was on a threshold, and by invoking a higher resource—a wilderness woman of great courage and strength to face the demon that represented fear—the fear was diminished.

Darcy then turns around and, embracing the wounded one, offers it care and nurturing. Then she embraces the dragon, who has been released, saying she feels exhausted and tired after such a long battle over many years. However, she comes to see and can embrace this dragon energy as a vehicle of freedom and renewed energy in her life.

During the following week, Darcy continues to practice what she has learned in the session by invoking the wilderness woman, nurturing the vulnerable one when needed, and by allowing time for resting.

Reflecting on the Session

This was a powerfully rich session. Darcy is richly descriptive in her expression and I am being constantly extended in order to hold a clear picture of what is going on. Steiner reassures me when he says, "This healing of the soul cannot be achieved by means of abstract theories and thoughts; these are too meagre and inadequate...Something that is strong in its effect, however, is what lives in our soul when we ponder on a picture or an Imagination that we have called up before our soul."[3] Darcy has made a huge step toward self-care, as it has been ten years since her mother was killed and the last time when she honored her own needs. For Darcy to reclaim her space and boundaries for her own wellbeing is monumental.

Who is the "dragon"? It could be an over-harnessed masculinity; her inner man is going mad, the wild man in the woman needing to be expressed. The depression is probably a response to being "tethered." The fear is a response to the "demon." Who then is the "demon"? It is possibly the spirit who possessed her schizophrenic brother, the dislocation of the "I"—that is, an inner place is vacant and no one is home, so

3 Steiner (1999a:69).

invites in the demon energy. The client is tethering her power. Dragon mythology is about powerful male energy.

Session 3: Spiritual Reconnection

Darcy says she no longer feels tethered to her depression, and is feeling a lot freer; a space has been created. Over the past few weeks Darcy had been experiencing images of the horror of her mother's death, like she is reliving it, as though she is holding on to the horror. Darcy sees the wounded self as like the painting "The Scream." A terror scream, in which she feels she had to contain the horror at the time of her mother's death in order to function and survive. Darcy goes into feeling and a deeper realization emerges in which she is holding onto the horror because it is the last memory of her mother, and she is afraid to let go because she does not want to let go of her mother. The following poem describes the horror of her mother's death.

Leaving Home

Fragmented pieces of skull
A mother does not make
And yet
I cannot shake
This image

Was the blood red
As it spurted from your head
And did you shed
A tear
As death drew near
And who was it for

What noise does a hammer make
On a human head?

Did you not know what hit you?
Instantly dead

As the policeman has said
Or was the slate kitchen floor
A cool soothing companion?
Your last moments of life
I can share only in supposition
in haunted visions
I dare not ask my brother
of this other
side of mother
but one day
when old enough
I might

Cruel retribution that would be
And yet it's not that
Just curiosity
that wants to look over the precipice of fear
hold her near
and see
this intimate snapshot of my mother
known by nobody but my brother

Baby boy trying to leave the nest
like all the rest
Journey on dear one
So alone
You've now left home
("Darcy" 2007)

The common picture became "Holding on for grim life, afraid to let go." This relationship to her mother is not okay; she feels stuck. Darcy makes a wish: "To hear the inner voice of the wounded one." She enters into the process straight away, as she is feeling the terror in her body now, in the guts. She enters into gesture, crouching down with her hands on her head, and screams . . . after coming out of this experience, she says she felt the terror and felt as though she was being hit by a hammer on the back of her head—this is how her mother died—and sees the skull shattering into many pieces. She hears the voice of the wounded one and feels guilty. She holds herself responsible for her mother's death, as she chose to withdraw support from her brother who had schizophrenia at this time.

Darcy then wants to explore her guilt, and when she enters into this experience, I suggest she speak from this position. Darcy tells the wounded one she is responsible for the death of her mother and brother, and when she exits and beholds this experience, she has a different perspective and instead feels great empathy for the wounded self, that she is not responsible for her mother's death, but is responsible for her own healing. Exposing the guilt itself brings Darcy to a place of compassion, and feeling enormous relief. She then says (second wish): "The wounded one needs healing and needs to find a new way to connect to her mother."

Darcy invokes the qualities of "Mother Mary" to offer healing to the wounded one, and she embraces herself in this experience with deep feeling for about ten minutes. As the counselor holding this space, I feel a strong presence in the room, particularly the presence of strong feminine energy. After this time, Darcy tells me that she felt the presence of "Mother Mary," and all the woman ancestors in her family, as golden light, joining hands in a circle, and felt her mother's presence. It felt like they were nourishing her with their golden light. Then, as the healed one, she stands up and says she needs the sound "mama," which she sang first and then she wanted to receive it, so I sang this sound to her. The session is completed, and during the following week Darcy is to spend time developing and growing this spiritual relationship with her mother.

Reflecting on the Session

Darcy's experiences in this session were of across the threshold. Also, when she crouches down, with hands over her head, screams, and the skull shatters, she experiences herself as her mother. Darcy is stuck in terror because her mother is stuck in terror, and in this situation, I became the midwife in her process. A few days later, Darcy had a session with a healer, which reaffirmed our therapy session, and she adds her own reflection that her understanding is her brother had killed himself in order to aid their mother on her spiritual journey after death: "With my journey to this point, synergistically there was movement and the healing image of my brother standing behind my mother with his arms protectively around her. The love was immense and both the [healer] and I felt tears in our eyes. I knew we, as a family, all felt released at this moment."

Session 4: Wild Witch Woman

Darcy describes the last time she felt a connection to her spirituality:

> I remember when driving home that my last consistent meditation practice was sending golden light to all the family members, before mum died and when all was sucked into a black hole. I remember my mum's friend saying that mum felt happy and that she looked as if she was surrounded and supported by love in the days before she died. Maybe the golden ones were with her. For the first time since then, I begin to feel as if something solid has returned, not just a lot of coping mechanisms that can be shattered like a pack of cards, like a human skull, like my psyche. This image of the golden ones and the power of mother earth heal my core and I feel as if a healing cornerstone has been laid and now I can begin to build and have confidence that under stress I won't collapse into mental ill health. My destiny may now unfold... When I need female guidance, I can rely on the women in the ancestor circle to direct me. I can let go of my unfulfilled expectation for other women to play my mother's role. I can let go of the disappointment and anger... If I can release mum in a celebration of joy, dragon will get its energy in a new way, not feeding off the pain body as before.

Darcy is now committed to staying anchored in her own truth and spirituality, to bringing more joy, fulfillment and happiness into her life. Darcy has been experiencing backache over the past few days and is not sure what it is about, as it is unusual for her to get back pain. Her wish is: "I would like to know more about this ache in my back and what it is trying to tell me." To explore the back pain, Darcy gestures the sensation, and when she exits, she beholds herself as a wild witch woman in the days of heresy, being staked in the back: "There is a stake being driven into my back as though I am to be destroyed." Further exploration reveals that when she is engaged with her spirituality and expressing her feminine essence, she is labeled, and now it feels like there is a stake in her.

> I have a flash of an image of a wild witch woman. I gesture the ache in my back and it is a stake being driven into my back as if I am a demon to be destroyed. I am placed on a fire to burn. This is a past-life recollection or a tapping into the female collective pain body from heresy days, when a nature-loving, animal-loving woman like myself was a target for hatred. Female energy was annihilated and repressed. Ever so slowly feminine energy emerges again and mother earth needs the feminine even more so now. I can see the bigger picture unfold. I am empowered to stay strong in my truth and rise again as witch, wild free woman and earth. This sense of advocacy really strengthens my resolve to stay truthful and awaken my own consciousness and my part to help heal the collective pain. I feel as if this behind aggressive energy is about to steamroll me. I raise my hands in the halt, stop stance and practice growling Bahhhh...Later the words "back off" will come to me as the forceful command. I must do this out loud and within, to situations tied to the past energy of fear and violence.

Darcy makes another wish: "I want to remove this stake." We move into a process of removing the stake, by wrenching it out with the sound "aarg" and throwing it onto the ground. Darcy feels a sharp pain when pulling the stake out and I ask her to check if there is anything else she needs. Closing her eyes, she says she needs to bathe the wound in pink healing light, with the sound "um ma." After doing this, all pain in her back has gone.

Reflecting on the Session

Another option in the process could be to create a meeting between Darcy now and the inner aspect, which still thinks she is in a past incarnation, to affirm her soul survived. This can bring a sense of the peace of death into the turmoil of the physical dying for those people who see the human being as comprising a body, soul and spirit.

Session 5: Deep Intimacy is My Birthright: A Session of Appreciation

Darcy has been spending more time in nature connecting to her spirituality and describes one occasion when she went out into the bush on her property at night:

> I see myself as a five-pointed star and the moon as my muse (inspiration: goddess). The moon of course is feminine energy and I have always felt an alignment with the moon but forgot this in my fear of the moon and the disturbed state that would come to my brother with schizophrenia...so wonderful to reconnect my love and intimate relationship to the moon. The moon energy energizes.

Darcy feels her heart opening with deep feeling for others: "Deep intimacy with others and me is my birthright." Her creative energy is growing and she is feeling for the first time that she has the courage to write about the death of her brother, the death of her mother, and about her brother's incarceration. Darcy shares and reads some of these poems and a short story about her brother in prison. This session was one of sharing and appreciating the journey so far. The following is one of Darcy's poems:

Survivor guilt

Give me a gun so I may say
Blow away my head
is what you said
precious brother
as you waded out to sea
in intolerable agony

What image lay there?
Shattered skull of our mother
splintering the mental fabric of your brain
into torturous triggers
of self-blame
again
and again
and again

Buy some rope
Smoke some dope
Tie it loose
Make a noose
Hang it high
Then jump
I'm coming mama
Brave soldier
Is coming too
This time
I'll save you

Darling brother
You always knew
What we all knew
Just more keenly
More true

We are all to blame
For turning away
I just cannot stay
but will pray

for golden light
to aid your plight
is what we said
before she was dead

Little mother left alone
Deserted
Family ties perverted
By the war zone that is
Paranoid Schizophrenia
In a world that doesn't give a shit
Not one tiny bit

("Darcy" 2007)

Session 6: Deepening Relationships

Darcy feels energized, is having deeper and more intimate relationships with others and is holding clearer boundaries with people when needed. She feels deeply connected to her spirituality, to her joyful, creative and expressive self. The focus in this session becomes how she occasionally questions and doubts her inner authority. After discussing this and coming to the common picture that self-doubt is compromising her spirituality and relationships, her wish is "To grow truth and wisdom in the face of self-doubt."

Rudolf Steiner describes three beasts that we meet on the threshold of the spiritual world, acting as hindrances to overcome in our personal and spiritual development.[4] The qualities to develop in order to counter these beasts are: overcoming self-doubt of the spirit—we need to develop and mobilize creativity and clarity; overcoming self-hatred—we have to develop warmth, love and compassion; and facing fear of the spirit—we need to mobilize inner courage. In Psychophonetics, the process is called "Beasts on the threshold" and aims to transform hindrances by making a shift from past to future orientation, from growing

4 Steiner (1994a).

by healing the past to growing by mobilizing resources in a forward-looking approach.

Darcy remembers a recent time when she experienced self-doubt, senses the impact of this experience and becomes it in gesture. After seeing and describing this experience of self-doubt, which appears as a huge creature, I suggest she turn away from it and imagine a future self in a few years time who has overcome this situation of self-doubt. Darcy invokes and connects to her future self as a woman of truth and wisdom, thereby creating a new internal role model, and feels the strength within. Then she turns around again to face the self-doubt, and it becomes smaller. Standing in this position of truth and wisdom, Darcy speaks confidently and freely of awakening and deepening relationships. Growing these qualities is her ongoing practice at home. Darcy is progressing well using gesture and sound work between sessions and connecting deeply to her spirituality, so we organize a follow-up session in one month.

Comments—These sessions have been about growing woman's wisdom, and the dragon energy has been about the recovery and healing of the inner man. Rudolf Steiner states: "Spiritual knowledge should most certainly not be described as a fantasy. Spiritual knowledge strives to find real ways of alleviating the distress of soul"[5] and when we consciously transform these imaginations through the force of feeling flowing out into the world, there is a health-giving effect.

Concluding

Darcy attended twelve sessions in total. However, four months after the last session, she reconnected to explore her vocation and attended monthly sessions over the following year. After twelve years of unemployment, Darcy is now working as an integration aide at a primary school. This achievement also supports her continuing attendance at a writing course and her poetry writing. Darcy sees this journey as

5 Steiner (1999a:145).

becoming "freedom from the loop," and I leave the final words in this chapter to Darcy.

The New Dream

Arising from within
My beautiful Skin
Becomes smooth
Free
From poisonous wounds
Truth broke the crust
Forgiveness the balm
Self-love new growth
I am Divinity
Recreating
Joining
Piecing
A new dream
My masterpiece of love
("Darcy" September 2008)

Darcy reflects on her journey so far:

> The poems emerged as golden crumbs to follow on a healing creative journey home to my spiritual centre...The spirits of the forest sang to me and my interest in Earth religions, especially shamanism, was born. I joined a creative writing group to nurture myself as a poet and to step back into community. I saw Merri Hughes, a psychologist who specializes in holistic healing through Psychophonetics therapy...Now the foundation stone of a temple was laid rather than the pack of cards house that I had been managing and rebuilding for most of my life.
>
> The poems reveal my journey to the Goddess within and to my understanding of divine union. They reveal my shamanic quest, as an emerging poet, to know how to bring through essence from the mystery...as the poems emerged from my own intensity, I too would sit with them with a kind of heart listening, as Coleman Barks described waiting beside Rumi's poems as he endeavored to translate their truths.

My longing for intimate connection with others brought me home to the divine union god and goddess connection within myself... I believe Goddess energy is reanimating at a time when the Earth needs us all to renew our vision within and thus change the reflection without. I face my own life with excitement as to what has "emerged" is bringing. ("Darcy" March 2009)

Chapter 16

Menopause: In-spiriting the Hot Flush

Françoise Foster

Is menopause an opportunity for initiation into one's power? I chose to explore menopause and in particular, hot flushes, as I did not want to cross this threshold in a semiconscious way. I was approaching fifty and feeling at times different, powerful stirrings in my soul that I could not ignore. They came up as strong powerful energy currents pushing up from below and forcing me to stand more upright in my soul space; it was about speaking my truth, honoring who I am, making a new space for my needs and for my "being-ness" in the world.

When I let these words resonate in my soul, the image of the kundalini arises within. The serpent, as a symbol of the kundalini, lay there quiet and dormant, coiled in the space created by the sacrum. However, this serpent energy suddenly wakes up and stands, its body fully erect, and becomes an upraised serpent, a symbol of transformation. Could it be that the kundalini force, hot and fiery in nature, described as the storehouse and powerhouse of all the creative energy in the physical form not being used anymore in maintaining the female reproductive function, would actually rise and express itself in a different way in our bodies at menopause, giving us an opportunity to transform?

A Woman's Journey toward Menopause

During her lifespan, a woman is faced with many different changes, from being a young girl experiencing the first period, the body getting ready for reproduction and moods becoming more erratic, to a young woman encountering her sensuality and femininity in new relationships to her mother, having to care for and nurture another being, to a menopausal woman having to accept the changes in her body and find a new connection to her soul. This is quite a journey. Maybe menopause is an opportunity to learn something new about ourselves and who we are.

The changes at menopause affect a woman's life in all different ways. The predictable rhythm of the menstruation is now lost, the body is changing, an inner turmoil is experienced as we don't know where this is all going, and this is all very disorienting. This period can seem like an entrance into dark unknown places, initiating us into a new way of being.[1] Some women see menopause as a crisis; they associate it with getting old, losing sex appeal, being depressed and a little crazy, and they would do anything to avoid going through this transition.

Menopause can also be experienced as a time of healing. It gives us a chance to review our life and look at who we are and what we do. It encourages us to come home to ourselves. Transitions are opportunities to foster a sense of self more congruent with who we truly are. The journey can be painful, as we visit wounded and disowned parts of ourselves. But in the darkness and suffering, we always find a point of light, a promise of what we can become. We deepen our connection to our soul and spirit, to that part of us that is eternal and divine. This is the alchemy available to us human beings. For some of us, menopause can bring a major shift in our identity; it is partly because this is the end of our fertility and we see old age and death coming a step closer. We become more aware of our mortality and wonder how we want to

1 Fincher (1995:74).

live our life, and what type of contribution we want to make to our family, to our society.

There are many physical symptoms of menopause, including digestive disturbances, depression, insomnia, anxiety, headaches, heart palpitations and hot flushes. I will focus on hot flushes in this chapter, as about seventy to eighty-five percent of perimenopausal women experience hot flushes.[2]

Befriending and In-spiriting the Hot Flush

I will write about three women, ages forty-nine to fifty-four, who were suffering hot flushes as the main and most bothersome physical symptom of menopause, and who came for counseling to address this issue. As body symptoms and the psychosomatic meanings for each client are explored, the following working definition of "hot flush" is useful: "A woman feels a sudden sensation of warmth, with heat spreading over her face, scalp and chest area, and her body may also become red and perspire."[3]

The three clients all agreed individually to enter the experience of the hot flush and made a wish to explore what it was and if it could speak to them. I first asked them to close their eyes and remember the hot flush. I encouraged them to sense it with their hands to find out how it was moving. The more they did this, the more they became one with it and the more they found out about it. After they gestured and moved their experience, they all did a drawing of their experience of the hot flush.

Lee describes what she experienced as an energy coming up from her solar plexus: "It surges quickly, it feels hot and powerful, it ends up as a power surge in the brain, and it is red in color."

Janet explains that her hot flushes had changed, they used to come up from below, but now she experiences them in a different way: "It

2 Northrup (2006:126).

3 Northrup (2006:128).

comes from the core of my being (she points up to her upper torso), it comes in quietly, it's like steam coming out, it is yellow and cloudy and it travels slowly and just sits around. It makes me perspire, my head and my face feels hot."

Paula, like Janet, explains that her hot flushes have changed—they used to come up from her lower belly as an energy surge: "Now it's like heat coming in my face, it sits in the skin, it is red and hot and it makes me sweat," she says, holding her two hands in front of her face, showing me where the heat is sitting.

Drawing what they perceive through movement and gesture helps these women to observe the content of their experience, and brings more information about what happened. They enter the experience fully with their whole body, not just with their hands.

Entering the Experience

Lee feels vulnerable. Her sudden shyness is in contrast to the way she presents herself as extremely confident and outgoing. When checking with her to see if she needs anything in order to continue, she wants to move with her back to me. She moves her hands above her head through the air in a circular manner, with gentle, sensual and feminine gestures. She slowly relaxes into it, moving her whole body in the same way as she is moving her hands. Softly at first, some gentle sounds come out of her mouth; she then starts humming an Indian song. Her voice becomes louder and louder, while stamping her feet on the ground with the rhythm of the melody. Her inner beauty and radiance are shining through and the space feels sacred. She shares that this is the first time in her life that anyone has witnessed this vulnerable aspect of herself. She hasn't been in a relationship for more than twenty years and is now ready to move on and enter a different kind of partnership that includes mutual love and respect.

Janet starts to move her hands gracefully around her chest, coming from her heart and radiating out around her torso and her head. She says: "There is great power here, it's like the power of the sun. It is warm and incredibly powerful. It is amazing, it is lovingly waiting, and it is a gift." I comment: "It is lovingly waiting for" and she replies: "me to pay attention. It contains a lot of knowledge and wisdom, it is a powerhouse of life energy, it's my life. I've come so far away from my center, from myself."

She goes on speaking about her childhood, saying that there was no safe place; there were always a lot of arguments and violence between her parents. When she grew up, she was treating herself in a detached, destructive and harmful way. Janet speaks about the time in her early twenties when she used to act and sing, was featured in a few movies and sang in jazz bands. She reflects: "I have not committed to the things that I love to do."

Paula started by squashing some invisible form. She furiously pushes it down, making it smaller and smaller. When she beheld the picture, she said, "I am the goddess of squashing and containing." I then suggest she become the squashed part. She slowly starts to move gently around and then begins running and jumping around the whole room, twirling with her arms outstretched, humming different sounds to accompany her movements. She looks totally enlivened by the process. When she stopped and observed this action, she saw herself as a goddess of power and said, "She is pulsating. She is a form maker and she's extremely powerful. She lives in the present moment. She creates and expresses."

There is an aspect of her that is powerful, rich, creative and expressive, but constantly being squashed and contained. Janet confirms that this inner dynamic is bringing anger and frustration. She feels the frustration of feeling she has failed as a mother of her teenage daughter and communication with her husband is poor, leaving her feeling powerless. She feels like she is going through the motions without being present in her life—that life is living her, instead of her living her life. During our conversation, Janet did not appear to be fully present in her body, but at the end of the session, after the action phase, she looks very different and says: "I feel lively and connected, my life is full of possibilities again."

Comments

Most women think that the symptoms of hot flushes or night sweats coming from their hormonal cycles are not connected to their actual life. As we can see with these three women, the symptom of the hot flush is a powerful messenger, telling them clearly that they were suppressing an aspect of their being. They had alienated a pocket of psyche in their soul and denied its expression.[4]

Healing the Wound, Strengthening the "I" and In-spiriting the Hot Flush

Lee—In another session, Lee presents with an issue related to her relationship with men. She says: "I keep attracting shit from men and it makes me feel worthless." Her wish is: "I want to love myself." She has discomfort in her belly and does a drawing of what is going on there. Lee colors the whole page with orange and in the middle of it she draws a dark spot. She enters the dark spot and becomes bent over as an intense pain emerges in her belly navel and moves to her left ovary. She describes it as a very dark, painful place with a cage around the ovary. When she enters the cage, she finds a little girl who had shut down from abuse.

She holds her and washes her with white light to dissolve the darkness. This cleansing ritual is facilitated by sounding "*LLL*." She also says that her inner child needs love and warmth. Lee invokes a divine mother figure within, holding the little inner girl for quite some time while speaking to her words of appreciation and care. When she is finished, she holds this inner girl in her heart.

When Lee came back for the next session, she said that she'd had a revelation during the week. She has been on various diets for losing weight, which were not successful. She remembered as a child making the decision to become chubby, as she understood her abuser did not

4 This finding is confirmed in Leysley Kenton's book *Passage to Power* (1995:125).

like fat girls. Lee is very excited to share this revelation and has been losing weight ever since without being on any diet. She now feels ready to take her power back. "I am a sexual being," she says. She has met a few men since her last session and is now able to sustain their gaze, whereas normally she would turn her head away. Lee is now being more in her adult self and staying present.

As she develops this relationship with her inner child, there is still a concern about feeling safe. There is still a need for some assurance that Lee, the woman, will not enter an abusive relationship. In an inner dialogue with her inner child, Lee commits to herself and her inner child that she will only become involved in a relationship that will be loving and honoring of herself, so that a feeling of reassurance and a stronger sense of safety is felt within her heart.

Janet—In another session, Janet expresses a lack of joy, focus and discipline in her life. She feels lonely and deeply unworthy. Addicted to finding the miracle remedy outside of self, she has been receiving more than six hundred emails per year from different spiritual groups. She expresses the wish: "to be more in touch with my heart." She enters her heart experience and becomes totally frozen. She experiences this as being in a container in space and becoming space trash. I invite her to come out and behold the scene. She starts to cry and says: "It is so sad... it's me now, me at twenty, me as a child, and she needs urgent care." Janet gives her inner self what she needs and comments: "she is starting to warm up; she also needs healing." She starts moving her hands over the body and says: "I'm not on my own, there are lots of spiritual helpers here, they are doing a better job than I am. The energies are starting to move in her body, it's going to take a few weeks for her to fully recover." Janet sounds "mmm," and then sang this for a long time: "she is much better, she is warm and the container has gone. She's still very fragile though," and holds her for a long time until she says: "she's alright now." Janet holds her inner self within her heart.

When I meet her for the next session, she looks different, appearing softer, warmer and more joyful. "*You look so different!*" I exclaim, to which she laughs and replies: "People at work usually don't come near me, I am normally left in my little corner all on my own, but this week they kept coming and wanting to talk to me." During the week she had nurtured herself by spending some quiet time on her own as well as dancing, singing and playing the drums. She feels more grounded, self-empowered and clearer about her boundaries, after having worked on this aspect in an earlier session. She has a twenty-four-year-old daughter suffering from bulimia and anorexia and it was coming to a point where she was rescuing her at the cost of her own needs. Janet had not seen her on the weekend and during the week had created a healing space to honor herself and her process. In this session she wants to appreciate the moment and share her insights with me. She expresses her need to join a singing and drumming group and says that her hot flushes are barely noticeable.

Paula—In this session, the presenting issue is about not making time for her own needs, keeping busy instead of creating a space to reflect. Her wish is: "I want to make choices that support me." Paula realizes that she keeps herself busy doing tasks such as housekeeping. In the action phase, Paula gestures what happens when she makes the choice between engaging in an activity or making time for herself. She crouches into a ball as if she wants to disappear and stays in that position for some time. She describes her experience of being in this space: "I feel like a beetle in suspended life. I don't have to do anything or participate in life. I'm not fully alive in here but it feels comfortable and safe." Paula realizes that the act of disappearing comes at a cost because she is missing out on life. She remembers being a little girl in a family of seven children and doing a lot of chores to please her mother. She then realizes that there is another being in the room—a huge, stern figure—and she feels belittled and inconsequential in his presence. As the counselor, I suggest she turn away from him and remember who she truly is. She says she is a spiritual being and firstly, she imagines becoming that being, then she does so in action by firmly planting her feet on the ground with arms outstretched toward the sky. She looks powerful and connected. Paula describes her body as being filled with a waterfall of sparkling light and states, "I matter." She then turns toward the figure once more, but it has now shrunk significantly. After completing this process, we speak about making choices and Paula is able to catch herself when she is listening to the voice that says "I'm inconsequential," and can replace it with "I matter."

I saw Paula for three more sessions and during this time she attended a workshop, which was held in nature where she connected with her inner life in a different way. She now feels more present in her soul through looking at nature, looking at a tree, admiring a flower or wondering at the beauty of a pod. She reflects on a previous session and shows me a picture of spiritual beings, which inspires her as it reminds her of her true nature. She feels ready to commit to a daily ritual, expressing the wish to go for a walk on her own, as this gives her a chance to reflect and be surrounded by nature.

Since completing the sessions, Paula has enrolled in a dance class and in a drawing class that does drawing from the inner life. She has also taken one day a week off work to dedicate to exploring her inner life and expression. This is a big change in her life.

Reflections and Conclusions

My interest was to see if menopause could be seen as a passage or initiation into power; however, I would now say that it becomes a passage in becoming more empowered by becoming more present in life if we are ready to embrace our inner life and have a relationship with it. One colleague said "hot flushes would be better renamed 'power surges' which gives the image of a positive transformative process."

All these three women were able to reclaim an aspect of their self that had been suppressed. This was a powerful experience for them. Lee reclaimed her sexuality, which had been locked in a wounded little girl. Janet reclaimed her heart, which had become frozen through lack of love and care by reconnecting to her creativity and expression. Paula found a new connection to herself and her inner life. They all entered this process through gesture, but it took each of them on their own unique journey.

The experience of the hot flush changed for all of them. With Lee, the hot flushes disappeared altogether. Janet's diminished so much they were hardly noticeable, and with Paula, the intensity and frequency of the hot flushes lessened. These physical symptoms became messengers for understanding and healing. Psychophonetics counseling is a powerful way to connect us directly with our inner experience and provides the capacity to enter experience deeply:

- Through sensing—the women were able to perceive the traces the hot flush had left in their subtle bodies.
- Through visualizing—they were able to create accurate pictures of what was happening in their inner experience.
- Moving, using their full body—they became one with the hot flush and found out exactly what it was expressing.
- Through beholding—they knew what the message was. It connected them immediately to painful, undigested pockets of experience emerging from their biographies. This was a turning point, as the unknown was made known.
- They could identify patterns of being that were not serving them any longer.
- They were able to create clearer boundaries and heal through using sound, invoking inner resources, calling on qualities they already had and resources from the spiritual world.

There are many approaches to dealing with menopause and in particular, to cooling hot flushes. Many women have found relief in practicing meditation, relaxation and yoga, as these practices can reduce stress hormones. Acupuncture, nutrition, herbs and plant-based hormones also can provide great support for women in alleviating the symptoms of hot flushes. Hormone replacement therapy (HRT) is a very common approach and for some this might be a necessity, but many women seem not to realize that menopause is a time of opportunity, when we can gain more insight about ourselves and clear some of the toxic, stuck emotions that are affecting our body biochemistry.

Through an experiential approach and artistic expression, the experience became meaningful for these clients. The body/psychosomatic approach with menopause symptoms is a powerful way for clients to know for themselves, and the hot flush can be seen as reminding us that something is suppressed or not acknowledged. It is important that the counselor create a sacred and safe space for the client to express the experience of the hot flush. In holding a space that honors the client, they can become radiant and alive, reconnecting with inner being: becoming "in-spirited." Expressing the hot flush brings a sense of wholeness and being in touch with something very precious in their inner being, contacting heart, spirit and creativity. Artwork such as painting and drawing are useful tools that stimulate the expression of flowing and creative movements. In addition to personal sessions, a group process is also very helpful for women to share their experiences together.

I now see menopause as a threshold that gives women another opportunity for healing, growing, becoming enriched, and in-spiriting their lives. Although we seem to lose some of our vital strength through aging, we gain a richer inner life to be shared with others. I am truly grateful to the women who continue to let me share their journey with them. They are an inspiration and a reminder of how magnificent, resilient and truly intelligent the whole human being is.

References

Alic, Margaret (2001). "Sexual Abuse." In *Encyclopedia of Psychology*. http://www.findarticles.com/p/articles/mi_g2699/is_0006/ai_2699000618 (October 2008).

Balson, Maurice (1988). *Becoming Better Parents*. Melbourne: Acer Press.

Bass, Ellen, and Laura Davis (1997). *The Courage to Heal: A Guide for Women Survivors of Child Sexual Abuse*. UK: Random House.

Bento, William. (2004). *Lifting the Veil of Mental Illness: An Approach to Anthroposophical Psychology*. Great Barrington, MA: SteinerBooks.

Bignell, Barry (2000). "Musical Utterance as a Way of Knowing: A Contemporary Epistemology of Music." Doctoral dissertation, University of Western Sydney.

Birch, Lea (1997). "Fortifying the Healing Process: Art Therapy for Children with Cancer." In Ian Gawler (ed.), *Science, Passion, and Healing: The Relationship between Mind, Immunity, and Health*. Yarra Junction, Australia: The Gawler Foundation (pp. 37–45).

Bloch, Sidney, and Bruce S. Singh (1995). *Understanding Troubled Minds: A Guide to Mental Illness and Its Treatment*. New York: NYU Press.

Bortoft, Henri (1996). *The Wholeness of Nature: Goethe's Way toward a Science of Conscious Participation in Nature*. Hudson, NY: Lindisfarne Books.

Bott, Victor (1984). *Anthroposophical Medicine: Spiritual Science and the Art of Healing*. New York: HarperCollins.

Burkhard, Gudrun (1997). *Taking Charge: Your Life Patterns and Their Meaning*. Edinburgh: Floris Books.

Crowley, Brian, and Ester Crowley (1994). *Words of Power: Sacred Sounds from East and West* (ch. 21, "Universal Sound"). Minnesota: Llewellyn Publications (pp. 281–294).

Dinkmeyer, Don. C., Gary D. McKay, and James S. Dinkmeyer (1989). *Parenting Young Children: Helpful Strategies Based on Systematic Training for Effective Parenting (STEP) for Parents of Children under Six*. Shoreview, MN: AGS Publishing.

Dunselman, Ron (1993). *In Place of the Self: How Drugs Work*. Stroud, UK: Hawthorn Press.

Dye, Sherelle (2008). *Spontaneous Regression: Surviving Cancer against the Odds*. Research Paper, Gawler Foundation. http://www.gawler.org/ (May 2010).

Egan, Gerard (2002). *The Skilled Helper: A Problem-Management and Opportunity Development Approach to Helping* (7th ed.). Pacific Grove, CA: Brooks/Cole, 2002.

Fincher, Susanne F. (1995). *Menopause: The Inner Journey*. Boston: Shambhala.

Gawler, Ian, ed. (1997). *Science, Passion and Healing: The Relationship between Mind, Immunity and Health*. Yarra Junction, Australia: The Gawler Foundation (pp. 37–45).

———. (2001). *You Can Conquer Cancer* (2nd ed.). Melbourne, Australia: Hill of Content.

———. (2008) Comments given at a book launch for *Surviving Cancer* (May 22). www.gawler.org (Accessed 20/9/08).

Gershom, Yonassan (1992). *Beyond the Ashes: Cases of Reincarnation from the Holocaust*. Virginia Beach, VA: A.R.E. Press.

Glöckler, Michaela (2000). *Sexual Abuse of Children*. Spring Valley, NY: Waldorf Early Childhood Association of North America.

Goleman, Daniel (1995). *Emotional Intelligence: Why It Can Matter More than IQ*. New York: Bantam.

Gottman, John (1997). *The Heart of Parenting: Raising an Emotionally Intelligent Child*. New York: Simon & Schuster.

Kenton, Leslie (1995). *Passage to Power: Natural Menopause Revolution*. New York: Hay House.

Kirkengen, Anna Luise (2001). *Inscribed Bodies: Health Impact of Childhood Sexual Abuse*. The Netherlands: Kluwer Academic Publishers.

Kübler-Ross, Elisabeth (1975). *Death: The Final Stage of Growth*. Upper Saddle River, NJ: Prentice-Hall.

Lachman, Gary (2003). *A Secret History of Consciousness*. Great Barrington, MA: Lindisfarne Books.

Lahey, J. (1993). "Cancer Gives Woman a Healthier Spirit." *The Age Newspaper* (11/9/1993).

Maciejewski, Paul K., Baohui Zhang, Susan D. Block, and Holly G. Prigerson (2007). "An Empirical Examination of the Stage Theory of Grief." *Journal of the American Medical Association* (JAMA) Vol. 297 (7). http://jama.ama-assn.org/cgi/reprint/297/7/716 (May 2010).

Marsh, Ali, and Ali Dale (2006). *Addiction Counseling: Content and Process.* Melbourne: IP Communications.

Members of ARTA Rehabilitation Centre. (1990). *Rock Bottom: Beyond Drug Addiction.* Stroud, UK: Hawthorn Press.

Northrup, Christiane (2006). *The Wisdom of Menopause: Creating Physical and Emotional Health and Healing During the Change* (2nd Edition). New York: Bantam.

Obsatz, Michael (2003). "From Shame-Based Masculinity to Holistic Manhood." http://www.angeresources.com/shamebased.html (May 2010).

Rothschild, Babette (2000). *The Body Remembers: The Psychophysiology of Trauma and Trauma Treatment.* New York: Norton.

Sardello, Robert (1995 [2007]). *Love and the Soul: Creating a Future for Earth.* New York: HarperCollins. Revised edition: *Love and the World: A Guide to Conscious Soul Practice.* Great Barrington, MA: Lindisfarne Books.

———. (1999). *Freeing the Soul from Fear.* New York: Riverhead.

Sauer, Jost (2006). "Marijuana Addiction." *Living Now Magazine* (7/06) Melbourne.

Schaef, Anne Wilson (1992). *Beyond Therapy, Beyond Science: A New Model for Healing the Whole Person.* San Francisco: HarperSanFrancisco.

Scharmer, Otto (2007) *Theory U: Leading from the Future as It Emerges.* Cambridge, MA: Society for Organizational Learning.

Sherwood, Patricia, and Yehuda Tagar (2000). "Experience Awareness Tools for Preventing Burnout in Nurses." *Australian Journal of Holistic Nursing,* 7(1), 15–20 (Refereed feature article).

———. (2000a). "Self-care Tools for Creating Resistance to Burnout: A Case Study in Philophonetics-Counseling." *Australian Journal of Holistic Nursing,* 7(2), 45–47.

Soesman, Albert (1998). *Our Twelve Senses: Wellsprings of the Soul.* N. Vancouver, BC: Steiner Book Centre.

Spock, Marjorie (1983). *Group Moral Artistry 2: The Art of Goethean Conversation.* Spring Valley, NY: St. George.

Steele, Robin (Chartres) (1996). "The Inner Dimensions of Parenting: Parenting and Self-parenting Skills." Paper in *The Second National Conference, Parenting in the 90s and Beyond: Helping the Next Generation Grow Conference Proceedings,* Melbourne, Australia.

———. (2004). "The Theory and Practical Application of Sounds in Therapy." *Psychotherapy in Australia Journal,* vol. 11, Nov (1), 66–71.

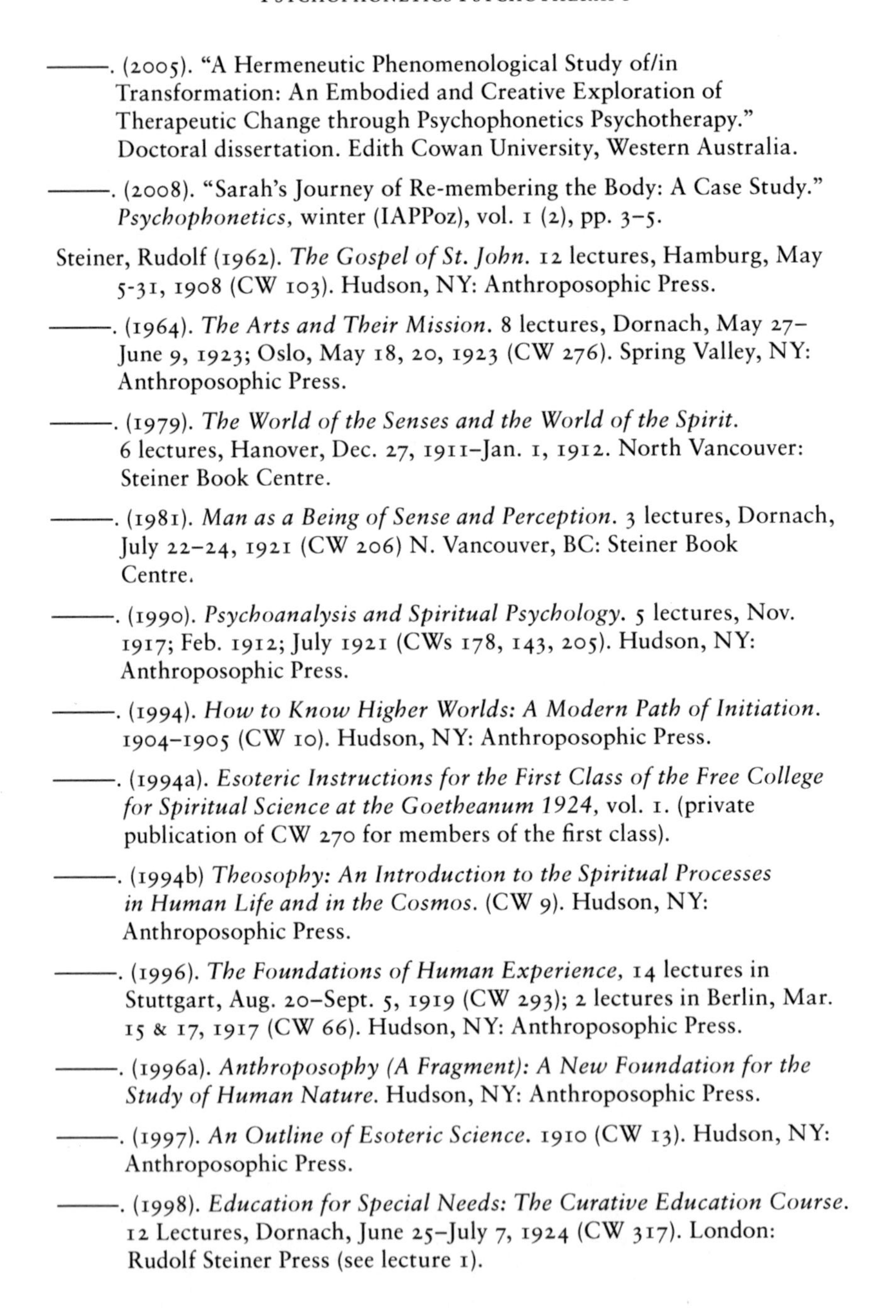

———. (2005). "A Hermeneutic Phenomenological Study of/in Transformation: An Embodied and Creative Exploration of Therapeutic Change through Psychophonetics Psychotherapy." Doctoral dissertation. Edith Cowan University, Western Australia.

———. (2008). "Sarah's Journey of Re-membering the Body: A Case Study." *Psychophonetics,* winter (IAPPoz), vol. 1 (2), pp. 3–5.

Steiner, Rudolf (1962). *The Gospel of St. John.* 12 lectures, Hamburg, May 5-31, 1908 (CW 103). Hudson, NY: Anthroposophic Press.

———. (1964). *The Arts and Their Mission.* 8 lectures, Dornach, May 27–June 9, 1923; Oslo, May 18, 20, 1923 (CW 276). Spring Valley, NY: Anthroposophic Press.

———. (1979). *The World of the Senses and the World of the Spirit.* 6 lectures, Hanover, Dec. 27, 1911–Jan. 1, 1912. North Vancouver: Steiner Book Centre.

———. (1981). *Man as a Being of Sense and Perception.* 3 lectures, Dornach, July 22–24, 1921 (CW 206) N. Vancouver, BC: Steiner Book Centre.

———. (1990). *Psychoanalysis and Spiritual Psychology.* 5 lectures, Nov. 1917; Feb. 1912; July 1921 (CWs 178, 143, 205). Hudson, NY: Anthroposophic Press.

———. (1994). *How to Know Higher Worlds: A Modern Path of Initiation.* 1904–1905 (CW 10). Hudson, NY: Anthroposophic Press.

———. (1994a). *Esoteric Instructions for the First Class of the Free College for Spiritual Science at the Goetheanum 1924,* vol. 1. (private publication of CW 270 for members of the first class).

———. (1994b) *Theosophy: An Introduction to the Spiritual Processes in Human Life and in the Cosmos.* (CW 9). Hudson, NY: Anthroposophic Press.

———. (1996). *The Foundations of Human Experience,* 14 lectures in Stuttgart, Aug. 20–Sept. 5, 1919 (CW 293); 2 lectures in Berlin, Mar. 15 & 17, 1917 (CW 66). Hudson, NY: Anthroposophic Press.

———. (1996a). *Anthroposophy (A Fragment): A New Foundation for the Study of Human Nature.* Hudson, NY: Anthroposophic Press.

———. (1997). *An Outline of Esoteric Science.* 1910 (CW 13). Hudson, NY: Anthroposophic Press.

———. (1998). *Education for Special Needs: The Curative Education Course.* 12 Lectures, Dornach, June 25–July 7, 1924 (CW 317). London: Rudolf Steiner Press (see lecture 1).

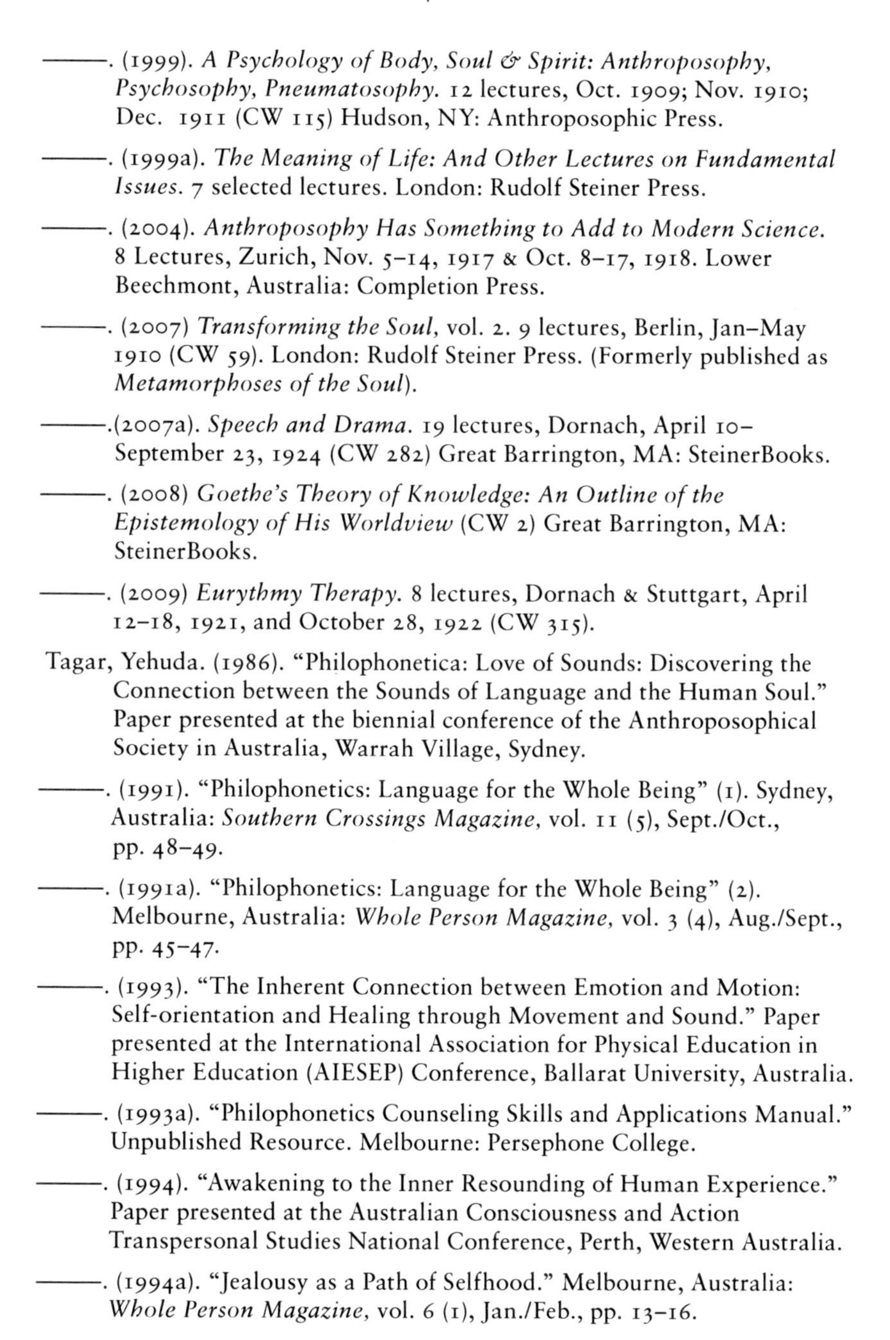

———. (1999). *A Psychology of Body, Soul & Spirit: Anthroposophy, Psychosophy, Pneumatosophy.* 12 lectures, Oct. 1909; Nov. 1910; Dec. 1911 (CW 115) Hudson, NY: Anthroposophic Press.

———. (1999a). *The Meaning of Life: And Other Lectures on Fundamental Issues.* 7 selected lectures. London: Rudolf Steiner Press.

———. (2004). *Anthroposophy Has Something to Add to Modern Science.* 8 Lectures, Zurich, Nov. 5–14, 1917 & Oct. 8–17, 1918. Lower Beechmont, Australia: Completion Press.

———. (2007) *Transforming the Soul,* vol. 2. 9 lectures, Berlin, Jan–May 1910 (CW 59). London: Rudolf Steiner Press. (Formerly published as *Metamorphoses of the Soul*).

———.(2007a). *Speech and Drama.* 19 lectures, Dornach, April 10–September 23, 1924 (CW 282) Great Barrington, MA: SteinerBooks.

———. (2008) *Goethe's Theory of Knowledge: An Outline of the Epistemology of His Worldview* (CW 2) Great Barrington, MA: SteinerBooks.

———. (2009) *Eurythmy Therapy.* 8 lectures, Dornach & Stuttgart, April 12–18, 1921, and October 28, 1922 (CW 315).

Tagar, Yehuda. (1986). "Philophonetica: Love of Sounds: Discovering the Connection between the Sounds of Language and the Human Soul." Paper presented at the biennial conference of the Anthroposophical Society in Australia, Warrah Village, Sydney.

———. (1991). "Philophonetics: Language for the Whole Being" (1). Sydney, Australia: *Southern Crossings Magazine,* vol. 11 (5), Sept./Oct., pp. 48–49.

———. (1991a). "Philophonetics: Language for the Whole Being" (2). Melbourne, Australia: *Whole Person Magazine,* vol. 3 (4), Aug./Sept., pp. 45–47.

———. (1993). "The Inherent Connection between Emotion and Motion: Self-orientation and Healing through Movement and Sound." Paper presented at the International Association for Physical Education in Higher Education (AIESEP) Conference, Ballarat University, Australia.

———. (1993a). "Philophonetics Counseling Skills and Applications Manual." Unpublished Resource. Melbourne: Persephone College.

———. (1994). "Awakening to the Inner Resounding of Human Experience." Paper presented at the Australian Consciousness and Action Transpersonal Studies National Conference, Perth, Western Australia.

———. (1994a). "Jealousy as a Path of Selfhood." Melbourne, Australia: *Whole Person Magazine,* vol. 6 (1), Jan./Feb., pp. 13–16.

———. (1994b). "The Methodology of Experience-Awareness" (unpublished resource). Melbourne: Persephone College.

———. (1995). "Philophonetics—Love of Sounds: New Faculties of Self-knowing and Healing." *Australian Naturopathic Practitioners & Chiropractors Association Journal*, vol. 2 (3), 22–23.

———. (1995a). "Empowerment, Maintenance, and Care for the Carer." Paper presented at the Pathways to Healing: Enhancing Life through Complementary Therapies, Royal College of Nursing Australia Conference, Canberra.

———. (1995b). "Revelations from the Inside: Reclaiming the Essential Connection, Its Beauty, and Its Joy." Adelaide, South Australia: *Golden Age Magazine*, no. 25, May/June, pp. 29–31.

———. (1995c). "Compassion: A Path of Self-healing." Adelaide, South Australia: *Golden Age Magazine*, July/August, pp. 25–28.

———. (1996). "The Healing Power of Expression with Philophonetics Counseling." In Ian Gawler (ed.), *The Mind–Body Connection*. Yarra Junction, Australia: The Gawler Foundation (pp. 239–250).

———. (1996a). "The Golden Coin of Now: The Present Moment as a Starting Point for Healing." Adelaide, South Australia: *Golden Age Magazine*, no. 29, Feb./Mar., pp. 21–24.

———. (1996b). "Caring for the Child Within: The Possibility, the Theory, and the Practice of Self-parenting Skills." Adelaide, South Australia: *Golden Age Magazine*, no. 31, June/July, pp. 21–24.

———. (1996c). "My Journey to My True Vocation: The Creation of Philophonetics-Counseling." Melbourne, Australia: "*Diversity*," *Natural & Complementary Health Magazine*, no. 8, July.

———. (1996d). "Re-creating Heart Safety." *Australian Anthroposophic Medicine Association (AAMA) Newsletter* 1 (Aug), pp. 3–4.

———. (1996e). "The Healing Power of Expression: Cancer as a Threshold of Inner Healing." In Ian Gawler (ed.), *The Mind–Body Connection Conference Proceedings*. Yarra Junction, Australia: Gawler Foundation (pp. 239–250).

———. (1997). "Cooperating with the Life Forces Within: A Possibility Inspired by Anthroposophical Medicine and Demonstrated by Philophonetics-Counseling." In Ian Gawler (ed.), *Science, Passion and Healing*. Yarra Junction, Australia: The Gawler Foundation (pp. 167–181).

———. (1998). "Vocation and the Will." Video of a lecture. Melbourne: Persephone College Resource.

———. (1998a). "Addictions: From Addictions to Real Needs." Video of a lecture. Melbourne: Persephone College Resource.

———. (1999). "The Use of Non-verbal Expression in Stress Management: With Philophonetics-Counseling." In Ian Gawler (ed.), *Medicine of the Mind*. Yarra Junction, Australia: The Gawler Foundation. pp. 245–266.

———. (1999a). "Fundamentals of Philophonetics Methodology of Sound Work." Unpublished resource. Melbourne: Persephone College.

———. (2000). "Participatory Therapy: Non-verbal Communication and the Healing Team of Client, Therapist, and Life-Body." In Marc Cohen (ed.), *Pathways to Holistic Health*. Clayton, Victoria: Monash Institute of Public Health. pp. 163–182.

———. (2001). "Philophonetics-Counseling: A New Perspective on Clients' Experience of Past Sexual Abuse and Its Application in Psychotherapy." Paper presented at the first South African conference for psychotherapy. South African Association for Psychotherapy (SAAP), Grahamstown, South Africa: Rhodes University.

———. (2003). "Psychophonetics in South Africa." In Ntomchukwu Sylvester Madu (ed.), *Contributions to Psychotherapy in Africa*. Polokwane (Pietersburg): UNIN Press. pp. 91–118.

Treichler, Rudolf (1989). *Soulways: Development, Crises, and Illnesses of the Soul*. London: Hawthorn Press.

van Houten, Coenraad (1995). *Awakening the Will: Principles and Processes in Adult Learning*. London: Temple Lodge.

Vogt, Felicitas (n.d.). *Drugs and Addiction: Prevention through Education*. Stuttgart: International Association of Waldorf Kindergartens.

Wehr, Gerhard (2002). *Jung and Steiner: The Birth of a New Psychology*. Great Barrington, MA: SteinerBooks.

Wolfert, Alan D. (1998). *Healing Your Grieving Heart: 100 Practical Ideas*. Fort Collins, CO: Companion Press.

Zeylmans van Emmichoven, F.W. (1982). *The Anthroposophical Understanding of the Soul*. Spring Valley, NY: Anthroposophic Press.

Index

Resources in the Field of Psychophonetics

International Association of Psychophonetics Practitioners (IAPP)

IAPP is a nonprofit incorporated association in the Republic of South Africa, with its headquarters in Cape Town, South Africa and with branches in Melbourne, Australia, and Stroud, UK. The *International Association of Psychophonetics Practitioners* seeks to promote the study of Philophonetics and Psychophonetics counseling/psychotherapy and its practice. It also seeks to advance the ethical practice of Psychophonetics across a range of settings encouraging human, environmental and spiritual wellbeing. It seeks to create, maintain and to develop a professionally based association that is inclusive, representative, holistic, and respectful on all levels of being.

IAPP is an association of professionals who are qualified as practitioners of Philophonetics and Psychophonetics counseling/psychotherapy or who have qualified with an award for applied Psychophonetics in a specialized field. IAPP maintains the register of authorized Psychophonetics training institutes and colleges, and registered Psychophonetics practitioners, supervisors and trainers.

Secretary—Katherine Train: kathyf@netpoint.co.za

Australian Psychophonetics Practitioners Group: www.psychophonetics.com.au

Persephone Institute

To qualify as a Psychophonetics practitioner, a three-year professional training course has to be completed, either through Persephone Institute in Cape Town (South Africa), or one of its branches at Persephone

College in Melbourne (Australia), or in Stroud (UK). The core of the training is based on four teaching blocks of eight days each per year for three years, plus regular peer-group meetings and supervised practicum in the second and third years between teaching blocks. In Australia and Cape Town, the course can also operate as weekly classes with some intensive weekends.

A Foundation Year course is offered for personal development, which is the first year of the professional training. There is also the opportunity for some people completing the three-year training to apply the Psychophonetics methodology in their own profession rather than become a counselor, for example, in coaching, business, other therapies, education, the arts.

South Africa

Persephone Institute
kathyf@netpoint.co.za
www.persephone-institute.com

United Kingdom

Persephone College UK
uk@psychophonetics.com
www.psychophonetics.co.uk

Australia

robin@psychophonetics.com.au
www.psychophonetics.com.au

Psychophonetics Publications

The first public presentation about Philophonetics/Psychophonetics was in 1986, when Yehuda Tagar presented the paper "Philophonetica: Love of Sounds: Discovering the Connection between the Sounds of Language and the Human Soul" at the conference of the Anthroposophical Society in Australia, in Sydney. Since then, many more articles and papers have been published in journals, books, conference proceedings, magazines and newsletters. A number of research master's and doctoral theses have been completed by Psychophonetics practitioners, with others currently in progress. Many of the articles and papers about Psychophonetics are referenced throughout the chapters of this book. Copies of selected articles and papers are available on the website: www.psychophonetics.com.au.

The Psychosophy Fellowship

On November 5, 2010, an anthroposophic conference was held in Berlin to celebrate 100 years since Steiner gave his lectures on psychosophy as the basis for a spiritual psychology. At the end of the 2010 Berlin conference, the Psychosophy Fellowship was formed, with founding members from the UK, Europe, USA, Australia, and South Africa.

The fellowship is for practitioners and researchers working in therapy, education, arts, and social development who wish to cultivate the life of psychosophy in the fields of healing, education and the arts in their own work and in society in general on the basis of Anthroposophy.

Practitioners who are working out of Anthroposophy and who are interested in cultivating psychosophy in the twenty-first century are welcome to join the Psychosophy Fellowship. To join the fellowship, contact Yehuda Tagar: tagar.yehuda@gmail.com.

Information about Psychosophy Seminars and courses:

The UK and Europe: Yehuda Tagar, www.psychophonetics.co.uk
North America: William Bento, Ph.D., www.psychosophyseminar.org
Australia: Robin Steele, Ph.D., www.psychophonetics.com.au

About the Authors

Adrian Hanks: advanced diploma in Psychophonetics counseling/psychotherapy; graduate of the Australian NSW Rural Communities Leadership Program; cert. IV AWT; cert. IV Anthroposophical Studies; member of IAPP. Adrian has been involved with many anthroposophically based initiatives since 1992 and trained as a Psychophonetics practitioner in Australia and in South Africa. He is a qualified adult educator and works with adults in personal development areas, to support, encourage and guide them toward their true potential. Adrian works in private practice from his studio in Bangalow, NSW, and across Australia and overseas. Adrian's unique *Eco-Soul Bush Therapy,* or *Therapy in the Bush*, incorporates Psychophonetics to guide people to explore, discover and transform their life questions and issues. Adrian is married with a blended family of six children, and in 2010, he published his first children's book, *Wendy and the Fairy Ring Secret,* the first of a series. Adrian is currently writing his first book on personal development for adults.. He is also working with his wife Arleen to complete a book on couple's relationships. Email: adhanks@bigpond.net.au; Website: www.consciouslifedevelopment.com.

Anne Holland: B.A.; diploma in education; advanced diploma in Psychophonetics counseling/psychotherapy; member of IAPP. Anne is an experienced teacher/trainer, educator and counselor. She worked in secondary schools and university for many years, in innovative education and in creating inclusive curriculums and policies. As an educational consultant, she has presented at conferences and facilitated workshops for teachers, as well as being the author of a published manual for teachers. Anne has been working in the personal development field for many years, with some years as the coordinator of Persephone College in Melbourne. She has a deep commitment to supporting people's learning and development. Anne recently worked with indigenous university students and currently provides training for supervisors and managers in the workplace. She has a private counseling practice, offering personal counseling sessions, as well as workshops and short courses. Anne's passion is grappling with Anthroposophy and how to work with that wisdom, using creative expression, as a way to explore and express what is meaningful in life. Email: anneholland@optusnet.com.au; website: www.psychophonetics.com.au.

Arleen Hanks: B.Ed. in music; advanced diploma in Psychophonetics counseling/psychotherapy; practitioner and teacher of Life Alignment Technique; member of IAPP. Arleen has studied various modalities of healing and self-development processes for over fourteen years in her homeland of South Africa. Arleen has now settled in Bangalow, NSW with her husband Adrian and blended family and works across Australia and overseas. She is also a practitioner and teacher of Life Alignment Technique and incorporates both her knowledge and skills of Psychophonetics and Life Alignment to offer clients a wide range of choice in their consultations. Her life in South Africa has given her a unique and special understanding of working with people's deeper spiritual issues and questions. Email: hanksa@bigpond.net.au; Website: www.consciouslifedevelopment.com.

Françoise Foster: diploma in remedial massage; certificate in relaxation massage; advanced diploma in Psychophonetics counseling/psychotherapy; member of IAPP. In addition to being a Psychophonetics practitioner, Françoise has studied other forms of healing such as pranic and energy healing, and spiritual healing. She also teaches French to children individually and in small groups. Françoise has extensive experience in living and working with life-threatening diseases and has a special interest in working with life transitions, such as menopause. Françoise facilitates short courses in personal development, such as, Healing the Chakras and has a counseling practice in

Camberwell, Melbourne. Email: foster.family@optusnet.com.au; website: www.psychophonetics.com.au.

Jillian Fowler: B.A.; diploma in social studies from Melbourne University; diploma in holistic counseling; advanced diploma in Psychophonetics counseling/ psychotherapy; professional memberships: AASW and IAPP. Jillian comes to holistic counseling from a background in social work practice (child and family health and welfare) and is the mother of four, mainly adult children (two having completed a Steiner Education). Jillian initially worked in Australia and the UK as a social worker for many years in a variety of areas, such as the children's court, the children's hospital, foster care and the child development unit in London. Jillian has given community talks and workshops, as well as presenting papers at Australian and international conferences, and has had articles published in journals. Jillian has been working with Psychophonetics for over ten years and facilitates the short courses, "Exploring Biography: Discover Meaning in your Life Patterns." Jillian currently has a part-time counseling practice in Melbourne. Email: jillfowler@optusnet.com.au; website: www.psychophonetics.com.au.

Judy Greenberg: assoc. diploma in arts (Welfare Studies); advanced diploma in Philophonetics counseling; advanced diploma in holistic counseling; professional memberships: AIWCW and IAPP. Judy is a counselor/psychotherapist in private practice in Melbourne and for a number of years she worked as a teacher and supervisor at Persephone College. Her background is in welfare work and using the experience of illness accompanied by "deep" remembering as a path for personal transformation and growth. Judy has a special focus on recovery from sexual abuse, chronic fatigue syndrome, psychosomatic illness, grief and loss. She also has an interest in the impact of inner peace on peace between individuals, within groups and in communities. This interest involves her with interfaith and social-justice organizations. Judy has presented her work to a variety of organizations in Australia as well as overseas, in Switzerland, Israel and Cyprus and is writing a book on her experience of the healing journey. Judy also facilitates personal development courses: "Restoring Inner Peace" and "Embracing Wholeness." Email: judyemma1@gmail.com; website: www.psychophonetics.com.au.

Linda Hall: Master of psychology (artistic counseling); diploma in Philophonetics counseling/psychotherapy; advanced diploma in holistic counseling; B.A.; diploma in education; professional memberships: IAPP and AAMA. After being in Singapore for five years, Linda is now based in Adelaide, South Australia. She is the director and trainer for Artbeat Education, a Singaporean initiative for adult training and children's therapeutic playgroups. Linda has more than thirty years of experience working as an educator, healing arts practitioner, psychotherapist/counselor and consultant. For twenty-five years, Linda worked as a volunteer with recovering addicts and for nearly twenty years has been involved in research, with a team in South Australia, examining the impact of nutritional factors in illness and health. Linda has taught counseling and artistic therapies at a number of institutions in Australia and in Asia: she has worked for the Brahm Education Centre and Sophia Course Works in Singapore, the Global Village Association in Macau, and the Metta Welfare Centre in Sri Lanka. Linda has a private counseling practice and conducts professional and personal development courses, workshops, as well as therapeutic classes in play and artistic activity for adults, adolescents and children. She also offers Steiner-inspired play groups for parents and children, and trains parents and child-care workers in creative discipline. Dedicated to non-intrusive and holistic methods in therapy and education, Linda was featured in a 2007 Singapore Mediacorp Channel 8 documentary: "No such thing as a bad kid." Email: linda.artbeat@gmail.com; website: www.artbeateducation.com.au.

Merri Hughes: graduate diploma in applied psychology; B.A.; diploma in welfare; advanced diploma in Psychophonetics counseling/psychotherapy; professional memberships: MAPS and IAPP. Merri has worked as a psychologist since 1995, with the last ten years in private practice. Prior to private practice, Merri worked for three years as a psychologist in family services for a community organization in Darwin, NT, Australia. She lived and worked in Arnhem Land for two years, where she developed an understanding of cultural issues, particularly those relating to indigenous people. Merri initially worked for some years in private practice in Lennox Head, NSW, and since 2000 has been working in the Yarra Valley in the outer eastern region of Melbourne. Merri, a mother of two children, is dedicated to conscious parenting and embraces the overall health and wellbeing of children as a potential way to create a more peaceful world. Email: merri.hughes@bigpond.com; website: www.merrihughes.com.au.

Rebecca Croad: advanced diploma in Psychophonetics counseling; cabinetmaker; beauty therapist; Reiki practitioner, levels 1 and 2; Swedish body massage; member of IAPP. Rebecca is a working, single mother of three active, healthy children and is involved as a coach in children's sports. She worked in energy work for a number of years and about eight years ago, she had a calling to work with people as a counselor. Her many experiences with grief and loss drew her into specializing in this area, and Rebecca currently maintains her work as a cabinetmaker while working part-time as a counselor in Sorrento, on the Mornington Peninsula. Email: rebeccacroad@netspace.net.au; www.marlospa.com.au/gunam.html.

Robin Steele: Ph.D.; M.Ed.St.; B.Ed. (EC); diploma of Philophonetics counseling practitioner; advanced diploma in holistic counseling; certificate adult teaching/learning; certificate IV in workplace assessment/training; certificate couples' therapy; clinical and professional memberships: PACFA (Reg.), SCAPE, AAMA, and IAPP. Robin Steele is a mother, teacher, educator, and counselor/psychotherapist working with people of all ages. Robin sees life as a journey of learning and is passionate about encouraging and inspiring people into becoming who they are. The qualifications, experience, knowledge and skills gained over many years give breadth and depth to her life and work. Robin's work of more than twenty years as an early-childhood teacher and supervisor of teacher trainees led to a change of career in the early 1990s to become a counselor/psychotherapist. She worked for several years at the Melbourne Therapy Centre and at the Clayton Whole Health Medical Clinic, as well as in private practice. Alongside counseling, she worked for several years as a college coordinator, teacher, and supervisor of trainee counselors at Persephone College in Melbourne. Robin has presented papers and workshops on Psychophonetics at conferences and has had articles and papers published. In 2005, Robin completed an anthroposophically based doctoral research thesis on the holistic nature of therapeutic change and transformation. She also had a book published in 2010, *The Effects of Encouragement: On the Development of Social Interest and Group Cohesiveness*. Robin is a professional supervisor and maintains a private psychotherapy practice, as well as being a facilitator of personal development courses such as The Healing Power of Sound. Robin is the mother of three grown children and grandmother of four. Email: robin@lifeways.net.au; website: www.lifeways.net.au.

Susan Morrison: B.A. in artistic counseling; diploma in transpersonal counseling; advanced diploma in holistic counseling (Philophonetics); advanced diploma in holistic counseling (artistic therapies); certificate IV in workplace assessment/training; clinical and professional memberships: IAPP, PACAWA, and PACFA (Reg). Susan has been practicing counseling and psychotherapy since the mid-1990s as well as designing and facilitating both therapeutic and educational groups using Psychophonetics since 2000. She is an experienced senior counselor working in a nongovernment agency in Perth, in the mental health field. She particularly works with recovering addicts in therapeutic communities, as well as working as a supervisor in private practice. Susan has a broad background in Western esoteric studies, and in particular Anthroposophy. She is currently completing a Master of Counseling degree at Notre Dame University in Fremantle, Western Australia. Email: suzanmorrison@bigpond.com; website: www.psychophonetics.com.au.

Yehuda Tagar: B.A. (ed. theater); postgraduate diploma in social sciences (counseling); graduate certificate in Anthroposophy, foundation year (Emerson College); certificate IV in workplace assessment/training; professional memberships: SAAP, WCP-AC, AMASA, and IAPP. Yehuda Tagar is an Israeli/Australian psychotherapist, trainer, and lecturer based in Cape Town, South Africa, and Stroud, UK. He is the founder of Philophonetics and Psychophonetics and is the principal of Persephone Institute. Yehuda has lectured internationally since 1991. He has taught extensively and presented papers and workshops at conferences in Australia, England, Israel, parts of Europe, and South Africa. He has had a number of papers published as well as many articles in magazines and journals. Yehuda primarily works as a teacher/trainer in the three-year professional counseling courses in Psychophonetics in Cape Town, South Africa and in Stroud, England. Email: yehuda.tagar@psychophonetics.com or tagar.yehuda@gmail.com; website: www.psychophonetics.co.uk.

Lightning Source UK Ltd.
Milton Keynes UK

174742UK00004B/2/P